CHRISTINE STAMM
LINDA CULLEN

On Cooking

A Textbook of
Culinary Fundamentals

Sarah R. Labensky
Alan M. Hause

DRAWINGS BY STACEY WINTERS QUATTRONE

PRENTICE HALL
ENGLEWOOD CLIFFS, NEW JERSEY 07632

Acquisitions editor: ROBIN BALISZEWSKI
Editorial assistant: ROSE MARY FLORIO
Supplements acquisitions editor: JUDITH CASILLO
Marketing manager: RAMONA SHERMAN
Cover design: RUTA KYSILEWSKYJ
Cover photograph: RICHARD EMBERY
Copyeditor: NANCY VELTHAUS
Manufacturing manager: ED O'DOUGHERTY
Director of production and manufacturing: BRUCE JOHNSON
Managing editor: MARY CARNIS
Production editor: PATRICK WALSH

Printed in the United States of America
10 9 8 7 6 5 4 3 2 1

ISBN 0-13-196627-8

Prentice-Hall International (UK) Limited, *London*
Prentice-Hall of Australia Pty. Limited, *Sydney*
Prentice-Hall Canada Inc., *Toronto*
Prentice-Hall Hispanoamericana, S.A., *Mexico City*
Prentice-Hall of India Private Limited, *New Delhi*
Prentice-Hall of Japan, Inc., *Tokyo*
Simon & Schuster Asia Pte. Ltd., *Singapore*
Editora Prentice-Hall do Brasil, Ltda., *Rio de Janeiro*

CONTENTS

ABOUT THE AUTHORS

Chef Christine Stamm is an Assistant Professor at Johnson & Wales University in Providence, Rhode Island, where she teaches a variety of courses in the Associate of Science and Bachelor of Science degree programs in culinary arts. Outside of teaching, she serves as a foodservice consultant and lecturer. She is currently pursuing her doctoral degree in education at Boston University.

Linda Cullen is an experienced culinarian, having held positions as chef manager and head chef in various establishments. Linda holds a Bachelor of Science degree in foodservice management and a Master of Science degree in managerial technology. For the past two years, Linda has been active in the Newport chapter of the American Culinary Federation, where she was editor of the chapter communique and is currently secretary.

In addition, Linda is a certified Culinary Educator. She has won awards for her culinary skill, including winning a gold medal at the prestigious International Culinary Exhibition at Torquay in England.

CHAPTER 1

PROFESSIONALISM

Cookery is a noble profession with a rich history and one steeped in tradition. This chapter provides an overview of the chefs that played an important role in the development of culinary arts, discusses their contributions, and then identifies the important attributes that a professional chef should possess and maintain.

At the end of this chapter the student should be able to:

1. Discuss the development of the modern foodservice industry.
2. Name key historical figures responsible for developing foodservice professionalism.
3. Explain the organization of a classical kitchen brigade.
4. Discuss the role of the professional chef in modern foodservice operations.
5. Identify the attributes a student chef needs to become a professional chef.

KEY TERMS

Cooking	Point
Cookery	Nouvelle cuisine
Professional cooking	Brigade
Carême	Gastronomy
Grande cuisine	Gourmet
Escoffier	Gourmand
Cuisine classique	Gourmet foods

TEST YOUR KNOWLEDGE

The practice sets provided below have been designed to test your comprehension of the information found in this chapter. It is recommended that you read the chapter completely before attempting these questions.

A. Terminology

Fill in the blank spaces with the correct term.

1. _____ Heat energy transfer to food in order to alter a food's texture, flavor, aroma and appearance.

2. _____ A cuisine for the French aristocracy and upper classes that was rich and elaborate, and emphasized strict culinary principles that distinguished this style of cooking from regional or "traditional" cooking.

3. _____ A master of simplicity and refinement in cooking whose work was carried to greater heights by a generation of chefs he trained including Bocuse, the Troisgros brothers, Chapel, Bise, Outhier, Guerard, and Verge.

4. _____ A late 19th and early 20th century refinement and simplification of grande cuisine that emphasizes thorough exploration of culinary techniques and principles.

5. _____ The master of French *grande cuisine* whose writings almost single-handedly refined and summarized five hundred years of culinary evolution by analyzing cooking, old and new, and emphasizing procedure and order.

6. _____ The art and science of eating well.

Fill in the blank spaces with the correct definition.

7. Brigade _____

8. Gourmand _____

9. Nouvelle cuisine _____

_____

10. Professional cooking _____

11. Auguste Escoffier _____

_____

B. Fill in the Blank

Fill in the blank provided with the response that correctly completes the statement.

1. _____ is terminology used in reference to the foodservice industry to describe the area where guests are generally not allowed, such as the kitchen.

2. _____ is terminology used in reference to the foodservice industry to describe the area where guests are welcome and serviced, as in the dining room.

3. In _____ service, the entree, vegetables, and potatoes are served from a platter onto a plate by the waiter.

4. _____ is the French term that literally means "everything in its place."

C. Short Answer

Provide a short response that correctly answers each of the questions below.

1. List three (3) advantages that the introduction of the cast iron stove lent to professional, 19th century cooking.

   a. _____

   b. _____

   c. _____

2. List three (3) examples of food preservation and storage techniques that were developed in the 19th century.

   a. _____

   b. _____

   c. _____

3. List five (5) types of demographic information that may be helpful to a chef in determining what his/her clientele may desire or need.

   a. _____

   b. _____

   c. _____

   d. _____

   e. _____

4. List three (3) ways a professional chef can show pride in performing his/her job.

   a. _____

   b. _____

   c. _____

D. Defining Professionalism

A student chef should try to develop six basic attributes in readiness for his/her role as a professional chef. Fill in the blank with the term that best matches the definition given on the right. (Term choices: knowledge, skill, taste, judgment, dedication, and pride)

Term

1. _____

2. _____

3. _____

4. _____

5. _____

6. _____

Definition

The ability to make sound decisions such as what items to include on the menu; what, how much, and when to order food; and approving finished items for service; all of which can only be learned through experience.

The desire to continually strive for the utmost professionalism and quality in spite of the physical and psychological strains of being a chef.

A chef's ability to prepare flavorful and attractive foods that appeal to all senses and to the desires of his/her clientele.

The desire to show high self-esteem for one's personal and professional accomplishments by means of such details as professional appearance and behavior.

An ability developed through practical, hands-on experience that can only be perfected with extended experience.

The understanding of a base of information that enables a chef to perform each aspect of the job.

E. Matching

Match each of the brigade member in *List A* with the appropriate duty/responsibility in *List B*. Each choice in List B can only be used once.

List A

_____ 1. Saucier
_____ 2. Friturier
_____ 3. Potager
_____ 4. Garde-manger
_____ 5. Rotisseur
_____ 6. Poissonier

_____ 7. Patissier
_____ 8. Grillardin
_____ 9. Boucher
_____ 10. Boulanger

List B

a. Sautéed items and most sauces
b. Chocolate eclairs
c. Caesar salad
d. Poached sole with caper sauce
e. Veal stock
f. Grilled veal tenderloin with black bean sauce
g. Roast pork with apple chutney
h. Ground beef
j. French fries
k. Steamed asparagus with hollandaise sauce
l. French bread

F. True or False

For each question below circle either True or False to indicate the correct answer.

1. Aside from quickly preparing foods to order, a *short order cook* may serve much the same role as a tournant, having mastered many cooking stations.
   True   False

2. Today most well-run foodservice operations use the formal kitchen brigade system as the means for organizing the kitchen staff.
   True   False

3. Most issues in the foodservice industry that are brought to the forefront for discussion, such as nutrition and sanitation, are brought about by the government.
   True   False

4. It was not until the early 1900's that advances in transportation efficiency improved to the point where the foodservice industry finally began to expand.
   True   False

5. Cuisine bourgeois refers to the style of cooking used by middle-class home cooks.
   True   False

6. The biggest difference between establishments serving buffets is that restaurants charge by the dish whereas cafeterias charge by the meal.
   True   False

7. A chef that prepares effective "mise en place" is one concerned only with classical cuisine.
   True   False

8. Most consumers choose a restaurant or foodservice establishment because it provides quality service and food for a price they are willing to pay.
   True   False

9. Escoffier is credited with developing the kitchen brigade system used in large restaurant kitchens.
   True   False

10. Although sun-drying, salting, smoking, pickling, and fermenting are effective means of preserving foods, they were passed up for newer technologies due to the labor intensity of preparation.
    True   False

CHAPTER 2

FOOD SAFETY AND SANITATION

One of the most important responsibilities of foodservice workers is to supply food that is safe to eat. Anyone handling food or the equipment used for its preparation needs to know how food-borne illnesses are caused and how they can be prevented.

At the end of this chapter the student should be able to:

1. Identify the causes of food-borne illnesses.
2. Explain numerous ways to handle food in a safe manner.
3. Take appropriate actions to create and maintain a safe and sanitary working environment.

KEY TERMS

Biological hazard	Temperature danger zone
Chemical hazard	ph
Physical hazard	Parasites
Direct contamination	Viruses
Cross-contamination	Fungi
Bacteria	Clean
Pathogen	Sanitize
Intoxication	Sterilize
Infection	HACCP

TEST YOUR KNOWLEDGE

The practice sets provided below have been designed to test your comprehension of the information found in this chapter. It is recommended that you read the chapter completely before attempting these questions.

A. Terminology

Fill in the blank spaces with the correct term.

1. _____ To remove physical dirt.

2. _____ The transfer of microorganisms to foods and food contact surfaces by humans, rodents, or insects.

3. _____ Poisoning of the consumer can actually occur when the toxins produced by pathogenic bacteria are ingested. Such toxins cannot be seen, smelled, or tasted.

4. _____ The leading cause of food-borne illnesses in spite of only being single-cell microorganisms.

5. _____ A type of bacterial illness caused when live pathogenic bacteria are ingested and live in the consumer's intestinal tract.

6. _____ A measurement of the acidity or alkalinity of a solution or product.

7. _____ The contamination of raw foods, or the plants or animals from which they come, in their natural setting or habitat.

8. _____ The broad range of temperature (40 degrees F. to 140 degrees F.) at which bacteria thrives and reproduces the best.

9. _____ To reduce the pathogenic organisms to safe levels.

10. _____ The smallest known form of life that invades living cells of a host, takes over those cells' genetic material, and cause the cells to produce more viruses.

11. _____ Chemical substances that may cause danger to the safety of food.

Fill in the blank spaces with the correct definition.

12. Pathogen _____

13. HACCP _____

14. Biological hazard _____

_____

15. Sterilize _____

16. Fungi _____

_____

17. Physical hazard _____

_____

18. Parasites _____

B. Multiple Choice

For each question below, choose the one response that correctly answers the question.

1. Which of the following is *not* a necessity for bacteria to survive and reproduce.
    a. food
    b. time
    c. moisture
    d. sunlight

2. The federal government enacted legislation designed to reduce hazards in the work area and therefore reduce accidents. This legislation is called:
    a. Safe Jobs for Working Americans Act (SJWAA)
    b. Occupational Hazards Prevention Policy (OHPP)
    c. Safety and Health for Working Americans (SHWA)
    d. Occupational Safety and Health Act (OSHA)

3. Choose the statement that accurately defines potentially hazardous foods.
    a. Foods used to prepare less popular menu items that require longer storage and therefore may promote bacterial growth.
    b. Various food products that have been sliced with the same knife on the same cutting board without intermittent sanitizing.
    c. Foods high in protein that therefore may support bacterial growth without careful handling.
    d. The presence, generally unintentional, of harmful organisms or substances.

4. Choose the statement that accurately describes how frozen foods should be defrosted. Pull the product from the freezer and:
    a. microwave on high in a plastic pan deep enough to catch the moisture.
    b. thaw at room temperature in a pan deep enough to catch the moisture.
    c. thaw in a warming oven on a roasting rack.
    d. thaw under refrigeration in a pan deep enough to catch the moisture.

5. Foods that are considered acidic have a pH that is:
    a. at 7.0
    b. 8.5-10.0
    c. 0-below 7.0
    d. 10.0-14.0

C. True or False

For each question below circle either True or False to indicate the correct answer.

1. The time-temperature principle is one of the best rules to follow to control the growth of bacteria.
    True   False

2. The first thing that should be done when a pest infestation is discovered is to try to find the source.
    True   False

3. A contaminated food will have an unusual odor.
   True   False

4. Food handlers are a major cause for the spread of bacteria.
   True   False

5. A dish can be clean without being sanitary.
   True   False

D. Food-Borne Diseases Review

This section provides a review of information regarding food-borne diseases. Fill in the blanks provided with the response that correctly completes each portion of the statement. Below is a definition of each of the points needing answers for each question.

Organism: What type of organism causes the disease? Is it a bacteria, parasite, virus, fungi, mold, or yeast?

Form: Especially relevant to bacteria, what form does it take? Is it a cell, a toxin, or a spore?

Source: In what foods might this organism be found, or what is the source of the contaminant?

Prevention: How can an outbreak of this disease be avoided?

1. *Botulism*

   Organism: _____

   Form: _____

   Source: _____

   Prevention: _____

2. *Hepatitis A*

   Organism: _____

   Source: _____

   Prevention: _____

3. *Strep*

   Organism: _____

   Form: _____

   Source: _____

   Prevention: _____

4. *Perfringens or CP*

   Organism: _____

   Form: _____

   Source: _____

   Prevention: _____

5. *Norwalk Virus*

   Organism: _____

   Source: _____

   Prevention: _____

6. *Salmonella*

   Organism: _____

   Form: _____

   Source: _____

   Prevention: _____

7. *E. Coli or 0157*

   Organism: _____

   Form: _____

   Source: _____

   Prevention: _____

8. *Trichinosis*

   Organism: _____

   Source: _____

   Prevention: _____

9. *Anisakiasis*

   Organism: _____

   Source: _____

   Prevention: _____

10. *Listeriosis*

   Organism: _____

   Form: _____

   Source: _____

   Prevention: _____

11. *Staphylococcus*

   Organism: _____

   Form: _____

   Source: _____

   Prevention: _____

CHAPTER 3

*N*UTRITION

Chefs have always been expected to serve foods that are nutritionally balanced in terms of protein, carbohydrates, fat, fiber, vitamins, and minerals. This unwritten rule has been determined by the public's understanding of the correlation between good eating habits, good health, and longevity of life.

At the end of this chapter the student will be able to:

1. Identify categories of nutrients and explain their importance in a balanced diet.
2. Explain the evolution of the USDA food pyramid and its significance in planning nutritious menus.
3. Apply the information found on product nutrition labels.
4. Explain the effect storage and preparation techniques have on various foods' nutritional values.
5. Categorize the basic nutritional information presented in this chapter in order to encourage further research in this complex topic area.

*K*EY *T*ERMS

Essential nutrients	Metabolism
Calorie	Vitamins
Carbohydrates	Minerals
Fats	Ingredient substitutes
Proteins	Ingredient alternatives

*T*EST *Y*OUR *K*NOWLEDGE

The practice sets provided below have been designed to test your comprehension of the information found in this chapter. It is recommended that you read the chapter completely before attempting these questions.

A. Terminology

Fill in the blank spaces with the correct term.

1. _____ The replacement of one ingredient for the more nutritious characteristics of another that may offer different taste, texture, or appearance but will not compromise, although it may slightly change, the original taste of the dish. Although it does not taste the same, it should still taste good.

2. _____ Vital dietary substances that are not manufactured by the body, but are needed to regulate metabolism, and therefore must be supplied by food.

3. _____ A group of compounds composed of oxygen, hydrogen carbon, and nitrogen that are necessary for manufacturing, maintaining, and repairing body tissue and may also be used as an alternative source of energy. Each chain is constructed of various combinations of amino acids.

4. _____ A group of compounds composed of oxygen, hydrogen, and carbon atoms that supply the body with energy and can be classified as saturated, monounsaturated, or polyunsaturated.

5. _____ Inorganic micronutrients necessary for regulating body functions and proper bone and teeth structures. These cannot be produced by the body, but must be attained by eating certain plant materials or animals that have eaten such plants.

Fill in the blank spaces with the correct definition.

6. Essential nutrients _____

_____

7. Calorie _____

8. Metabolism _____

_____

9. Ingredient substitutes _____

_____

10. Carbohydrates _____

_____

B. Short Answer

Provide a short response that correctly answers each of the questions below.

1. List five things a food service worker can do to meet the diverse nutritional needs of the consumer.

   a. _____

   b. _____

   c. _____

   d. _____

   e. _____

2. Give three examples of unsaturated oils.

   a. _____

   b. _____

   c. _____

3. Give three examples of saturated fats.

   a. _____

   b. _____

   c. _____

4. Briefly discuss how you feel a chef should determine what and how many healthful food items should be included on a restaurant menu without limiting or "turning off" other guests.

   _____

   _____

   _____

   _____

   _____

   _____

   _____

   _____

C. Parts of a Food Label

Identify the six areas of importance on the food label format released as of July 1994. Briefly explain the significance of each.

a. _____

b. _____

c. _____

d. _____

e. _____

f. _____

Nutrition Facts

Serving Size ½ cup (114g)
Servings Per Container 4

Amount Per Serving

Calories 90	Calories from Fat 30

% Daily Value*

Total Fat 3g	**5%**
Saturated Fat 0g	**0%**
Cholesterol 0mg	**0%**
Sodium 300mg	**13%**
Total Carbohydrate 13g	**4%**
Dietary Fiber 3g	**12%**
Sugars 3g	
Protein 3g	

Vitamin A	80%	•	Vitamin C	60%
Calcium	4%	•	Iron	4%

* Percent Daily Values are based on a 2,000 calorie diet. Your daily values may be higher or lower depending on your calorie needs:

	Calories	2,000	2,500
Total Fat	Less than	65g	80g
Sat Fat	Less than	20g	25g
Cholesterol	Less than	300mg	300mg
Sodium	Less than	2,400mg	2,400mg
Total Carbohydrate		300g	375g
Fiber		25g	30g

Calories per gram:
Fat 9 • Carbohydrate 4 • Protein 4

Part of label	*Significance*
a. _____	_____
b. _____	_____
c. _____	_____
d. _____	_____
e. _____	_____
f. _____	_____

D. Nutrition Review

This section is designed to test your knowledge and therefore covers many different aspects of the chapter.

Match each of the items in *List A* with the appropriate letter *List B*. Each choice in List B can only be used once.

List A

_____ 1. Monosaccharides
_____ 2. Fats and oils
_____ 3. Protein
_____ 4. Water
_____ 5. Micronutrients
_____ 6. Fruit group

_____ 7. Vegetable group
_____ 8. Saturated fat
_____ 9. Food pyramid
        instituted by USDA
_____ 10. Bread, cereal, rice,
_____   and pasta group
_____ 11. USDA reduces seven
         food groups to four
_____ 12. RDA

List B

a. 1992
b. 9 kcal/gram
c. Simple sugars
d. 1956
e. 6-11 servings per day
f. Transports nutrients and wastes through body
g. 3-5 servings per day
h. Carbohydrates
i. Vitamins and minerals

j. 2-4 servings per day

k. Found mainly in animal products and tropical oils
l. Recommended Dietary Allowance
m. 2-3 servings per day

CHAPTER 4

MENU PLANNING AND FOOD COSTING

This chapter gives an in-depth explanation of one of the most important aspects of foodservice - the cost. The techniques used here to control costs and set prices are the basic ingredients for either success or failure in the foodservice industry.

After studying chapter 4 the student should be able to:

1. Describe the different types and styles of menus.
2. Explain the purpose of standardized recipes.
3. Calculate the cost per portion for recipes.
4. Convert recipe yield amounts.
5. Determine menu prices and calculate food cost percentages.

KEY TERMS

Entree	Table d'hôte	As-purchased	As-served
Static menu	Recipe	Total recipe cost	Food cost
Cycle menu	Standardized recipe	Cost per portion	Inventory
Market menu	Metric system	Edible portion	Prime cost
Hybrid menu	Food cost percentage	Yield factor	Yield
À la carte	Conversion factor	Trim loss	Parstock

TEST YOUR KNOWLEDGE

The practice sets provided below have been designed to test your comprehension of the information found in this chapter. It is recommended that you read the chapter completely before attempting these questions.

A. Terminology

Fill in the blank spaces with the correct term.

1. _____ The figure used to increase or decrease ingredient quantities for recipe yields.

17

2. _____ The term used to describe the minimum amount of stock necessary to cover operating needs between deliveries.

3. _____ A menu which offers an entire meal at a fixed price.

4. _____ The term for food cost plus direct labor cost, which is used to determine menu price.

5. _____ The most commonly used measuring system in the world.

6. _____ A method of storage that requires older food items to be used first.

7. _____ A recipe producing a specific quality and quantity of food.

8. _____ A menu which is influenced by market availability.

9. _____ The total cost of ingredients for a recipe, excluding overheads, labor, fixed expenses, and profit.

Fill in the blank spaces with the correct definition.

10. À la carte _____

11. Food cost % _____

12. Entree _____

13. Inventory _____

14. Recipe _____

15. Food cost _____

16. Unit cost _____

17. Trim loss _____

18. Yield _____

B. Units of Measure

Fill in the blanks for the following conversions.

1. 1 lb	=	_____ oz		
2. 1 oz	=	_____ g		
3. 1 lb	=	_____ g	=	_____ kg
4. 1 kg	=	_____ g		
5. 1 g	=	_____ oz		
6. 1 kg	=	_____ oz	=	_____ lb
7. 1 c	=	_____ tbsp	=	_____ fl oz
8. 2 pt	=	_____ qt	=	_____ fl oz
9. 2 qt	=	_____ gal	=	_____ pt
10. 1 c	=	_____ tbsp	=	_____ fl oz

C. Recipe Conversion

The following recipe presently yields 32 6-oz portions. Convert the quantities in the recipe to yield 28 6-oz portions and 40 8-oz portions. (Recipe 11.4, page 237)

NOTE: Remember to convert new yields back into pounds, ounces and quarts.

Cream of Broccoli Soup

	Old Yield	*New Yield I*	*New Yield II*
	6 qt. (6 lt)	_____	_____
	32 Portions	*28 Portions*	*40 Portions*
	6 oz each	*6 oz each*	*8 oz each*
Butter	3 oz	_____	_____
Onion	12 oz	_____	_____
Celery	3 oz	_____	_____
Broccoli	3 lb	_____	_____
Chicken velouté	4 qt	_____	_____
Chicken stock	2 qt	_____	_____
Heavy cream	24 oz	_____	_____
Broccoli florets	8 oz	_____	_____

D. Unit Costs

At present market value, calculate the following unit costs.

	A.P. Cost		*Unit Cost*
1. Mayonnaise	1 Case	1 Gal	1 Cup
	$_____	$_____	$_____
2. Tomato sauce	1 Case	1 Can	1 Cup
	$_____	$_____	$_____
3. Eggs	1 Case	1 Tray	1 Egg
	$_____	$_____	$_____
4. Apples	1 Case	1 Tray	1 Apple
	$_____	$_____	$_____

E. Recipe Costs

For each of the following six problems use the two figures that are given to calculate the missing figure on each line.

	Cost per Portion	*# of Portions*	*Total Cost*
1.	$1.75	25	$_____
2.	$_____	6	$5.10
3.	$1.95	_____	$23.40
4.	$8.50	75	$_____
5.	$_____	125	$806.25
6.	$5.50	_____	$220.00

F. Yield Factor and Percentage

Calculate the total yield weight, yield factor, and yield percentage for each of the following.

	A.P. Quantity	Trim Loss	Total Yield Wt.	Yield Factor	Percentage
1.	10 lb	2 lb	_____	_____	_____
2.	8 oz	1 1/2 oz	_____	_____	_____
3.	2 lb	5 oz	_____	_____	_____
4.	15 lb	3 lb 4 oz	_____	_____	_____
5.	25 lb	5 oz	_____	_____	_____
6.	50 lb	15 lb 2 oz	_____	_____	_____

G. Applying Yield Factors

Determine the E.P. (Edible Portion) unit cost of the following, using the same weights and yield factors that were calculated in section F.

	Weight	A.P. Cost	A.P. Unit Cost	Yield Factor	E.P. Unit Cost
1.	10 lb	$5.99	_____	_____	_____
2.	8 oz	$15.54	_____	_____	_____
3.	2 lb	$3.26	_____	_____	_____
4.	15 lb	$6.48	_____	_____	_____
5.	25 lb	$9.83	_____	_____	_____
6.	50 lb	$8.37	_____	_____	_____

H. Food Cost

Provide answers for each of the food cost problems below.

1. If sandwiches for the month of January cost $635 to make and sales totaled $1,750, what is the food cost percentage for sandwiches this month?
   Answer: _____%
2. If it costs 25 cents for 1 bowl of soup and the desired food cost percentage is 30%, what would the selling price be?   Answer: $_____
3. The food cost for sole meunière is $10.95. It takes 5 minutes to have the sole cleaned and skinned at a labor cost of $8.00 per hour.
   a. What is the prime cost?   Answer: $_____
   b. What is the selling price if the desired prime cost percentage is 40%?
   Answer: $_____
4. If 150 portions of apple pie were sold in the restaurant in the first week of January and the sales totaled $37.50, what would the selling price be if the desired food cost percentage was 25%?   Answer: $_____

CHAPTER 5

TOOLS AND EQUIPMENT

This chapter is a guide to the basic tools used in the foodservice industry. It emphasizes the importance of safety and use of the correct tool for the job. The following exercises will help you to understand the tools you will be working with and their many uses.

At the end of this chapter the student should be able to:

1. Recognize a variety of professional kitchen tools and equipment.
2. Select and care for knives properly.
3. Explain how a professional kitchen is organized.

KEY TERMS

NSF International	Stove
Knife	Oven
Thermometer	Work stations
Scale	Work sections
Strainer	Soyer

TEST YOUR KNOWLEDGE

The practice sets provided below have been designed to test your comprehension of the information found in this chapter. It is recommended that you read the chapter completely before attempting these questions.

A. Terminology

Fill in the blank spaces with the correct term.

1. _____ A standard that governs the design, construction, and installation of kitchen tools, cookware, and equipment.
2. _____ The most important item in the tool kit.

3. _____ A device used to measure temperatures in food, refrigerators, and freezers.

4. _____ An enclosed space where food is cooked, surrounded by hot dry air.

Fill in the blank spaces with the correct definition.

5. Stove top   _____

6. Work station   _____

7. Work section   _____

8. Soyer   _____

B. Equipment Identification

Identify each of the following items and give a use for each.

1. Name of item: _____

   Major use: _____

   _____

2. Name of item: _____

   Major use: _____

   _____

3. Name of item: _____

   Major use: _____

   _____

4. Name of item: _____

   Major use: _____

   _____

5. Name of item: _____

    Major use: _____

    _____

6. Name of item: _____

    Major use: _____

    _____

7. Name of item: _____

    Major use: _____

    _____

8. Name of item: _____

    Major use: _____

    _____

9. Name of item: _____

    Major use: _____

    _____

23

10. Name of item: _____

    Major use: _____

    _____

11. Name of item: _____

    Major use: _____

    _____

12. Name of item: _____

    Major use: _____

    _____

13. Name of item: _____

    Major use: _____

    _____

14. Name of item: _____

    Major use: _____

    _____

15. Name of item: _____

    Major use: _____

    _____

16. Name of item: _____

    Major use: _____

    _____

17. Name of item: _____

    Major use: _____

    _____

18. Name of item: _____

    Major use: _____

    _____

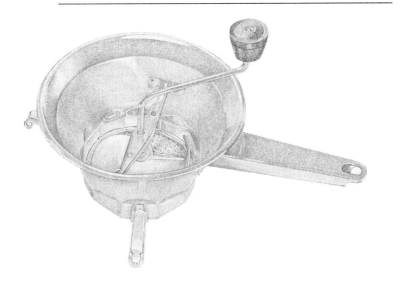

19. Name of item: _____

    Major use: _____

    _____

20. Name of item: _____

    Major use: _____

    _____

C. Matching

Match each of the pieces of equipment in List A with the appropriate letter definition in List B. Each choice in List B can only be used once.

	List A	*List B*
_____	1. Mandolin	a. Can be used in food up to 400° F (204° C).
_____	2. Refrigerator	b. The metal used most commonly for commercial small utensils.
_____	3. Candy thermometer	c. A metal that holds and distributes heat very well but is quite heavy.
_____	4. Salamander	d. Food is placed on a revolving spit.
_____	5. Copperware	e. An overhead broiler used to brown the top of foods.
_____	6. Rotisserie	f. A loosely woven cotton fabric used to strain sauces and stocks.
_____	7. Cast iron	g. The metal which is the most effective conductor of heat for cookware.
_____	8. Cheesecloth	h. Used for food storage, may be walk-in or reach-in.
_____	9. Tilting skillet	i. A manually operated slicer used for small quantities of fruit and vegetables.
_____	10. Aluminum	j. A piece of equipment that can be used for frying or braising.
		k. A metal that changes color when in contact with acid foods.

D. True or False

For each question below circle either True or False to indicate the correct answer.

1. Stem-type thermometers should be thrown away when they are dropped.
   True   False

2. Ventilation hoods should be cleaned and inspected by the hotel/restaurant maintenance staff.
   True   False

3. Some hand-made imported pottery may contain lead in the glaze.
   True   False

4. Class A fire extinguishers are used for fires caused by wood, paper, or cloth.
   True   False

5. High carbon stainless steel discolors when it comes in contact with acidic foods.
   True   False

6. A steam kettle cooks more slowly than a pot sitting on a stove.
   True   False

E. Short Answer

Provide a short response that correctly answers each of the questions below.

1. List three of the six requirements for NSF certification of kitchen tools and equipment.

   a. _____

   b. _____

   c. _____

2. Describe four important criteria for evaluation of equipment for kitchen use.

   a. _____

   b. _____

   c. _____

   d. _____

3. List and describe the three types of metals used in knife blades.

   a. _____

   b. _____

   c. _____

F. Fill in the Blank

Fill in the blank with the response that correctly completes the statement.

1. A _____ knife is used for general purpose cutting of fruits and vegetables.
2. The part of the knife known as the _____ is the part of the blade that is inside the handle.
3. Short order and fast food operations often use a flat metal surface known as a _____ on which to cook food.
4. A _____ _____ is useful for chopping large quantities of foods to a uniform size.
5. It is advisable to use _____ spoons when cooking with nonstick surfaces.
6. A butcher knife is also known as a _____.

CHAPTER 6

KNIFE SKILLS

Good knife skills are essential to maximizing efficiency and safety in the kitchen. This chapter outlines these important skills which should be practiced until they become second nature.

After studying chapter 6 the student should be able to:

1. Care for knives properly.
2. Use knives properly.
3. Cut foods into a variety of classic shapes.

KEY TERMS

Whetstone	Chopping	Medium dice
Steel	Dicing	Large dice
Slicing	Julienne	Paysanne
Chiffonade	Batonnet	Mincing
Rondelles	Brunoise	Tourner
Diagonals	Small dice	Oblique

TEST YOUR KNOWLEDGE

The practice sets provided below have been designed to test your comprehension of the information found in this chapter. It is recommended that you read the chapter completely before attempting these questions.

A. Terminology

Fill in the blank spaces with the correct term.

1. _____ An instrument used to straighten the blade of the knife between sharpenings.

2. _____ The smallest cube-shaped cut (1/8 inch x 1/8 inch).

3. _____ Also known as a sharpening stone.

4. _____ A wedge-shaped cut of vegetable.

5. _____ Finely shredded leafy vegetables used as a garnish or a base for cold presentations.

6. _____ A stick-shaped cut, slightly larger than julienne (1/4 inch x 1/4 inch x 2 inches)

7. _____ Round-shaped slices from a cylindrical vegetable such as a carrot.

Fill in the blank spaces with the correct definition.

8. Julienne _____

9. Small dice _____

10. Tourner _____

11. Medium dice _____

12. Mincing _____

13. Paysanne _____

14. Large dice _____

15. Diagonals _____

16. Chopping _____

B. True or False

For each question below circle either True or False to indicate the correct answer.

1. A sharp knife is more dangerous than a dull one.
   True   False

2. Tourner means "to turn" in French.
   True   False

3. A steel is used to sharpen knives.
   True   False

4. Batonnet are also referred to as allumette.
   True   False

5. A whetstone should be moistened with a mixture of water and mineral oil.
   True   False

6. Paysanne is a half-inch dice that has been cut in half.
   True   False

7. One should not attempt to catch a falling knife.
   True   False

8. Knives should not be washed in the dishwasher.
   True   False

C. Cuts of Vegetables

Draw the following cuts of vegetables to scale and describe their dimensions. Point out any similarities between the strips of vegetables and the cubes in the space provided below.

_____

_____

_____

_____

1. Julienne

4. Brunoise

2. Batonnet

5. Small dice

3. Paysanne

6. Medium dice

D. Fill in the Blank

Fill in the blank with the response that correctly completes the statement.

1. There are _____ methods of cutting, one where the _____ acts as the fulcrum and the other where the _____ acts as the fulcrum.
2. Parsley and garlic should be chopped with one hand flat on the _____ of the knife, using a _____ motion.
3. When cutting food always cut _____ from yourself and never cut on _____, _____, or _____ surfaces.
4. When using a whetstone start by placing the _____ of the knife on the stone. Start sharpening on the _____ side of the stone and finish with the _____ side.
5. An onion is diced by cutting in half and then making incisions towards the _____ of the onion, without cutting through it.

CHAPTER 7

KITCHEN STAPLES

A single, complete list of kitchen staples does not exist due to the varying needs of food-service establishments. Identifying common ingredients such as herbs, spices, nuts, oils, and vinegars that are used as staples can enable us to set forth standards of quality and storage.

After studying this chapter the student will be able to:

1. Identify and tastefully utilize a variety of herbs, spices, nuts, oils, vinegars, and condiments.
2. Prepare and serve good-quality coffees and teas.

KEY TERMS

Staples	Bouquet garni
Seasoning	Sachet
Flavoring	Onion piquet
Aromatic	Nut
Condiment	Oil
Herb	Vinegar
Spice	Decoction
Spice blend	Infusion

TEST YOUR KNOWLEDGE

The practice sets provided below have been designed to test your comprehension of the information found in this chapter. It is recommended that you read the chapter completely before attempting these questions.

A. Terminology

Fill in the blank spaces with the correct term.

1. _____ Boiling a substance until its flavor is removed.

2. _____ An item that adds a new taste to a food and alters its natural flavors.

3. _____ Recognizable combinations of spice flavors that are developed by countries and cuisines. These can be purchased as commercial blends, or can be mixed by the chef as needed.

4. _____ Used to introduce flavorings, seasonings, and aromatics into stocks, sauces, soups, and stews; it is made by tying a selection of herbs and vegetables into a bundle with twine.

5. _____ Any item added to a dish for flavor with a modern identity of cooked or prepared flavorings such as prepared mustards, relishes, bottles sauces, and pickles.

6. _____ The extraction of flavors at temperatures below boiling.

7. _____ The edible single-seed kernel of a fruit surrounded by a hard shell.

8. _____ A type of fat that remains liquid at room temperature.

Fill in the blank spaces with the correct definition.

9. Onion piquet _____

10. Herb _____

11. Spice _____

12. Staples _____

13. Vinegar _____

14. Flavoring _____

15. Seasoning _____

_____

B. Identification

Based on the two categories given, identify the items from the list below that are examples of each category. Fill in the blanks provided under each category heading with the corresponding examples.

Herb	*Spice*
1. _____	6. _____
2. _____	7. _____
3. _____	8. _____
4. _____	9. _____
5. _____	10. _____

paprika	oregano	lemon grass
cilantro	thyme	lavender
capers	garlic	coriander
black pepper	ground mustard	

C. Fill in the Blank

Fill in the blank provided with the response that correctly completes the statement.

1. Provide four characteristics by which coffee is judged.

   a. _____ refers to the feeling of heaviness or thickness that coffee provides on the palate.

   b. _____ will often indicate the taste of coffee.

   c. _____ refers to the tartness of the coffee, lending a snap, life, or thinness

   d. _____The most ambiguous as well as the most important characteristic, having to do with taste.

2. _____ is a commercial coffee bean from which the finest coffees are produced.

3. _____ is a bean which does not produce as flavorful a coffee, but is becoming more significant commercially since the trees are heartier and more fertile than their predecessors.

4. The best results for brewing a good cup of coffee are nearly always achieved by using _____ level tablespoons of ground coffee per 3/4 measuring cup (_____ ounces) of water.

5. A cup of _____ is often either the very first or the very last item consumed by a customer. _____, whether iced or hot, is often consumed throughout the meal.

6. _____, _____, and _____ are three types of vinegars.

D. Short Answer

Provide a short answer that correctly answers each of the questions below.

1. List and briefly explain five of the standard descriptions used with various types of coffee roasting.

   a. _____

   b. _____

   c. _____

   d. _____

   e. _____

2. List three guidelines to follow when experimenting with the use of different herbs and spices in various dishes:

   a. _____

   b. _____

   c. _____

3. Salt is the most basic seasoning and its use is universal. List three things salt can do for food.

   a. _____

   b. _____

   c. _____

4. List the three basic types of tea:

   a. _____

   b. _____

   c. _____

E. True or False

For each question below, circle either True or False to indicate the correct answer.

1. Green tea is yellow-green in color and partially fermented to release its characteristics.
   True   False

2. Ketchup originally referred to any salty extract from fish, fruits, or vegetables.
   True   False

3. In reference to making beverages, the term steeping means mixing hot water with the ground coffee.
   True   False

4. When preparing a recipe that calls for fresh herbs, the rule to follow when fresh herbs are unavailable is: use more dried herbs than the original fresh variety.
   True   False

5. A standard sachet consists of peppercorns, bay leaves, parsley stems, thyme, cloves, and optionally garlic.
   True   False

6. Mustard never really spoils, its flavor just fades away.
   True   False

7. The main difference between the three types of tea is the manner in which the leaves are treated after picking.
   True   False

8. Café latte is made by mixing 1/4 espresso with 3/4 steamed milk without foam.
   True   False

9. Whole coffee beans will stay fresh for a few weeks at room temperature whereas ground coffee will only stay fresh three or four days.
   True   False

10. A shortening is a fat, usually made from animal fats, and is solid at room temperature.
    True   False

CHAPTER 8

EGGS AND DAIRY PRODUCTS

Eggs, milk, and milk-based products, known collectively as dairy products, are extremely versatile in numerous culinary applications. Attaining the highest quality, and maintaining freshness through proper handling and storage, are critical.

At the end of this chapter the student should be able to:

1. Identify the composition of eggs.
2. Purchase and store eggs properly.
3. Identify, store, and use a variety of milk-based products.
4. Identify, store, and serve a variety of fine cheeses.

KEY TERMS

Yolk   Homogenization
Albumen   Certification
Chalazae cords   Clarified butter
Pasteurization   Fondue

TEST YOUR KNOWLEDGE

The practice sets provided below have been designed to test your comprehension of the information found in this chapter. It is recommended that you read the chapter completely before attempting these questions.

A. Terminology

Fill in the blank spaces with the correct term.

1. _____ Constituting just over one third of the egg and three fourths of the calories, it also contains most of the minerals and vitamins, all of the fat, and lecithin.

2. _____ A process performed to destroy the pathogenic bacteria by heating a liquid to a prescribed temperature for a specific period of time.

3. _____ These thick, twisted strands of egg white anchor the yolk in place and their prominence can be an indicator of freshness.

4. _____ The process of reducing the fat globules in size and permanently dispersing them throughout the liquid in order to ensure a uniform consistency, a whiter color, and a richer taste.

Fill in the blank spaces with the correct definition.

5. Certification _____

6. Fondue _____

_____

7. Albumen _____

8. Clarified butter _____

_____

B. Egg Composition

Identify the parts of the egg indicated in the following diagram and write their names in the spaces provided..

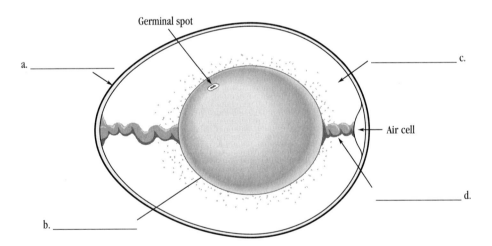

C. Matching

I. Match each of the cheeses in List A with the appropriate description in List B. Each choice in List B may be used only once.

List A	**List B**
_____ 1. Mozzarella	a. Britain's soft, blue-veined cow's milk cheese containing 45% fat.
_____ 2. American cheddar	b. A hard, cow's milk cheese containing from 32% to 35% fat and produced exclusively near Parma, Italy.
_____ 3. Parmigiano-Reggiano	c. A soft, creamy, goat's milk cheese with a short shelf life.
_____ 4. Gruyere	d. A pale yellow, Danish cow's milk cheese with many small, irregular holes, often made with herbs and spices.
_____ 5. Boursin	e. A fresh, firm, Italian cow's milk cheese very mild in flavor, and can become elastic when cooked.
_____ 6. Stilton	f. A French, rindless, soft, triple cream cow's milk cheese usually flavored with garlic, herbs, or peppers.
_____ 7. Chevre	g. A firm, cow's milk cheese made primarily in NY, WI, VT, and OR, 45% to 50% fat.
_____ 8. Fontina	h. A cow's milk, semisoft cheese from the Piedmont region of Italy having a few small holes and 45% fat.
_____ 9. Feta	i. An fresh, Italian or Greek sheep and/or goat's milk cheese that is white and flaky, pickled, and stored in brine.
_____ 10. Havarti	j. A firm, Swiss, cow's milk cheese that is highly flavorful, sweet and nutty, and aged up to 12 months.
	k. A sheep's milk cheese made from central and southern Italy containing approximately 35% fat.

II Match each type of cream in List A with the appropriate fat content in List B. Each choice in List B may be used only once.

List A	**List B**
_____ 1. light whipping	a. not less than 36% milkfat
_____ 2. light cream	b. 10%–18% milkfat
_____ 3. half and half	c. 16%–23% milkfat
_____ 4. heavy (whipping) cream	d. 18%–less than 30% milkfat
	e. 30%–36% milkfat

D. Multiple Choice

For each question below, choose the one response that correctly answers the question.

1. At what temperature does an egg yolk solidify (coagulate) when cooking?
   a. 135 degrees F.–143 degrees F.
   b. 120 degrees F.–132 degrees F.
   c. 160 degrees F.–171 degrees F.
   d. 149 degrees F.–158 degrees F.

2. Aside from increasing the shelf life of cream, the process of ultrapasteurization:
   a. reduces the whipping properties
   b. thickens the consistency
   c. causes the cream to stay whipped for longer periods of time
   d. concentrates the fat content

3. What would be a good use for grade B eggs:
   a. as a compound in facial creams and other cosmetic products
   b. for baking, scrambling, or the production of bulk egg products
   c. grade B eggs are not recommended for use in foodservice operations
   d. for frying, poaching, or cooking in the shell

4. Grades of milk are assigned based on:
   a. the clarity of color and distribution of fat globules.
   b. bacterial count; no less than 20 and no more than 30 per gallon earns a grade A.
   c. bacterial count; the lower it is, the higher the grade.
   d. the flavor of the milk as determined by the breed and feed of the animal.

5. Which four of the following are criteria for grading eggs?
   a. certification of farmer
   b. albumen
   c. spread
   d. shell
   e. breed of bird
   f. yolk

6. Clarified butter is whole butter with the water and milk solids removed by:
   a. melting it over high heat and then straining it through cheesecloth
   b. melting it with the inclusion of whipped egg whites, bringing to a simmer, and then removing the raft and impurities
   c. melting it over low heat, then chilling it quickly in order to clarify
   d. melting it over low heat, bringing it to a simmer, and then skimming

7. Evaporated milk, sweetened condensed milk, and dry milk powders are all examples of:
   a. canned milk products
   b. concentrated milk products
   c. cultured dairy products
   d. substandard milk products

8. One pound of whole butter that is then clarified will result in what volume of clarified butter?
   a. 10 oz
   b. 16 oz
   c. 8 oz
   d. 12 oz

E. True or False

For each question below circle either True or False to indicate the correct answer.

1. Egg whites solidify (coagulate) when cooked at temperatures between 144 degrees F. and 149 degrees F.
   True   False

2. Shell color has an effect on the grade of the egg, but not on flavor or nutrition.
   True   False

3. Eggs are a potentially hazardous food.
   True   False

4. All grades of milk must be pasteurized before retail sale.
   True   False

5. To ensure maximum volume when preparing whipped egg whites, the whites should be thoroughly chilled prior to whipping.
   True   False

6. Eggs should be stored at temperatures below 35 degrees F. and at a relative humidity of 70–80%.
   True   False

7. Both butter and margarine contain about 80% fat and 16 % water.
   True   False

8. Yogurt is a good example of a health or diet food.
   True   False

9. Margarine is a dairy product that serves as a good substitute for butter.
   True   False

10. Aside from excess moisture, processed cheese foods are of equal quality as natural cheeses.
    True   False

11. Egg substitutes can replace whole eggs in all applications.
    True   False

12. Natural cheeses contain cholesterol.
    True   False

CHAPTER 9

PRINCIPLES OF COOKING

During the cooking process, heat energy is transferred to foods by means of conduction, convection, or radiation. Understanding how cooking influences the molecular structure, appearance, aroma, flavor, and texture of foods is important in order to perfect these techniques.

At the end of this chapter the student should be able to:

1. Contrast and compare how heat is transferred to foods through conduction, convection, and radiation.
2. Identify how heat affects foods.
3. List and explain the procedures for using various cooking methods.

KEY TERMS

Conduction	Roasting	Blanching
Convection	Baking	Infrared cooking
Radiation	Sautéing	Pan-frying
Microwave cooking	Deep-frying	Induction
Poaching	Coagulation	Simmering
Gelatinization	Boiling	Caramelization
Steaming	Broiling	Braising
Grilling	Stewing	

TEST YOUR KNOWLEDGE

The practice sets provided below have been designed to test your comprehension of the information found in this chapter. It is recommended that you read the chapter completely before attempting these questions.

A. Terminology

Fill in the blank spaces with the correct definition.

1. Poaching
   _____ _____

2. Baking
   _____

3. Gelatinization
   _____

4. Radiation
   _____

5. Conduction
   _____

6. Blanching
   _____

7. Stewing
   _____

8. Pan-frying
   _____

9. Microwave cooking
   _____

10. Grilling
    _____

11. Steaming
    _____

Fill in the blank spaces with the correct term.

12. _____ A method of cooking that usually applies to meats and poultry and is the process of surrounding a food with dry, heated air in a closed environment.

13. _____ A cooking method whose dry heat is transferred by means of conduction. The method is performed by cooking relatively small cuts of food at high temperatures in a small amount of fat or oil.

14. _____ A term associated to what happens when proteins are cooked by the application of heat. The proteins will lose moisture, shrink, and become firm.

15. _____ The transfer of heat through a fluid, which may be liquid or gas.

16. _____ The food is submerged into a liquid held at temperatures between 185 degrees F and 205 degrees F and cooked.

17. _____ A dry-heat cooking method that uses convection to transfer heat to food completely submerged in hot fat.

18. _____ A moist cooking method using convection to transfer the energy from the liquid to the food. The large amount of liquid used to cook the food is brought to a rolling boil before completely submerging the food product to be cooked.

19. _____ A combination cooking method usually performed on larger pieces of foods, especially meats, that need tenderizing by cooking for long periods of time at a relatively low temperature. The liquid, which covers 1/3 to 1/2 of the product during cooking, is usually used to make the sauce that is served with the finished product.

20. _____ A dry cooking method using radiant heat that is applied from above the food product being cooked. The food being cooked is usually placed on a metal grade and is subjected to temperatures as high as 2000 degrees F.

21. _____ A new form of electric cooking that works when a coil below the cook stove's surface generates a magnetic current that reacts very quickly with special cookware made of cast iron or magnetic stainless steel.

22. _____ The process of cooking sugars where through the application of dry heat they turn brown and change flavor.

23. _____ Cooking that occurs when an electric or ceramic element is heated to such a high temperature that it emits waves of radiant heat that cook the food.

B. Cooking Methods

Fill in the spaces provided with the response that correctly completes information about each cooking method.

Cooking medium	Medium	Heat transfer method
ex: sautéing	fat	stove
1. Stewing	_____	_____
2. Deep fat frying	_____	_____
3. Broiling	_____	_____
4. Poaching	_____	_____
5. Grilling	_____	_____
6. Simmering	_____	_____
7. Baking	_____	_____
8. Roasting	_____	_____
9. Steaming	_____	_____
10. Braising	_____	_____

C. Multiple Choice

For each question below, choose the one response that correctly answers the question.

1. Which method refers to the transfer of heat through a fluid?
   a. convection
   b. radiation
   c. conduction
   d. induction

2. What cooking technique is an example of moist cooking?
   a. grilling
   b. sautéing
   c. deep-fat frying
   d. steaming

3. The purpose for the shape of the wok used for stir-frying is that the rounded shape:
   a. makes it easier to pour liquids out of it.
   b. is designed to fit into the specially designed shape of the turbo gas burners.
   c. diffuses the heat and makes tossing and stirring easier.
   d. makes the cookware more durable.

4. Which of the following is an example of infrared cooking?
   a. broiling
   b. sauteing
   c. roasting
   d. baking

5. In pan-frying, how much fat or oil should be in the pan?
   a. Just enough to coat the bottom of the pan
   b. 1 cup measure
   c. 1/2 to 2/3 way up on the product being cooked
   d. Enough to completely cover the product

6. What cooking technique is defined in the following statement: "To briefly and partially cook a food in boiling water or hot liquid."
   a. boiling
   b. blanching
   c. frying
   d. simmering

D. Short Answer

Provide a short response that correctly answers each of the questions below.

1. List the four major differences between braising and stewing

   Braising   **Stewing**

   a. _____   a. _____

   b. _____   b. _____

   c. _____   c. _____

   d. _____   d. _____

2. List two recommendations on how to properly steam a food product.

   a. _____

   b. _____

3. In five steps explain how to properly sauté a chicken breast.

   a. _____

   b. _____

   c. _____

d. _____

e. _____

4. Describe the six steps necessary for correct poaching of a food item.

a. _____

b. _____

c. _____

d. _____

e. _____

f. _____

E. Matching

I. Match each of the cooking methods in List A with the appropriate temperature in List B. Each choice in List B may be used only once.

List A	List B
_____ 1. boiling	a. 160 degrees F. to 180 degrees F.
_____ 2. broiling	b. 185 degrees F. to 205 degrees F.
_____ 3. simmering	c. up to 2000 degrees F.
_____ 4. poaching	d. 212 degrees or higher (at sea level)
_____ 5. steaming	e. 212 degrees F. (at sea level)
_____ 6. deep-fat frying	f. 212 degrees F. to 220 degrees F.
	g. 325 degrees F. to 375 degrees F.

II. Referring to the effects of heat on food, match the food categories in List A with the reactions in List B. Each choice in List B may be used only once.

List A	List B
_____ 1. starch	a. caramelize
_____ 2. water	b. gelatinize
_____ 3. fat	c. melt
_____ 4. protein	d. evaporate
_____ 5. sugar	e. coagulate
	f. permeate

CHAPTER 10

STOCKS AND SAUCES

Basic stocks and sauces are the foundations upon which the creative chef can experiment and build. The important of this chapter cannot be overemphasized as it explains the origins of sauces and how best to combine them with other flavors.

At the end of this chapter the student should be able to:

1. Describe the preparation of the basic stocks.
2. Classify sauces into their particular family.
3. Utilize thickening agents in the correct manner.
4. List a variety of classic and modern sauces and describe their preparation.

KEY TERMS

Stock	Venting	Monter au beurre
Sauce	Degrease	Demi-glace
Court bouillon	Deglaze	Jus lié
Mirepoix	Sweat	Emulsification
Connective tissue	Remouillage	Coulis
Cartilage	Roux	Chutney
Collagen	Beurre manié	Salsa
Gelatin	Liaison	Refresh

TEST YOUR KNOWLEDGE

The practice sets provided below have been designed to test your comprehension of the information found in this chapter. It is recommended that you read the chapter completely before attempting these questions.

A. Terminology

Fill in the blank spaces with the correct term.

1. _____ Tissue found in the animal's body that supports muscles.

2. _____ A sauce made from a mixture of chunky vegetables and herbs, whose name is the Spanish word for sauce.

3. _____ The French term for "rewetting" a stock to reuse the bones.

4. _____ A combination of half brown sauce and half brown stock which is then reduced by half.

5. _____ A protein which is found in connective tissue and dissolves during the cooking process.

6. _____ A flavored liquid, also known as a base.

7. _____ A sauce similar to demi-glace except that it is lighter and easier to make.

8. _____ Placing a stockpot in a sink of water to cool.

9. _____ Removing the fat off the top of a soup or stock.

10. _____ A thickened liquid used to complement and flavor foods.

11. _____ A mixture of onion, carrot, and celery used to enhance the flavor of stocks.

12. _____ A tough elastic tissue that helps give stucture to an animal's body.

Fill in the blank spaces with the correct definition.

13. Court bouillon _____

14. Gelatin _____

15. Chutney _____

16. Refresh _____

17. Emulsification _____

18. Liaison _____

19. Deglaze _____

20. Coulis _____

21. Monter au beurre _____

22. Beurre manié _____

48

23. Roux   _____

24. Sweat   _____

B. Stock-Making Review

Stock-making is a fundamental skill. The procedure for making basic stocks should be second nature to all good chefs.

List the essential ingredients and describe in a step-by-step manner the cooking procedure for white stock, brown stock and fish stock. Exact quantities are not important for this exercise, however, cooking times should be included and each step should be numbered for revision purposes.

White Stock

Ingredients: *Procedure:*

_____

_____

_____

_____

_____

_____

_____

_____

_____

_____

_____

Brown Stock

Ingredients: *Procedure:*

_____

_____

_____

_____

_____

_____

_____

_____

_____

_____

_____

Fish Stock

Ingredients: *Procedure:*

_____

_____

_____

_____

_____

_____

_____

_____

_____

_____

_____

C. Sauce Review—Mother Sauces

This section reviews the make-up of the five mother sauces. In the spaces provided below fill in the name of the sauce, the thickener used, and the liquid that forms the base of the sauce. For the sauces that use a roux as a thickener please specify the type of roux used.

	Mother Sauce	Thickener	Liquid
1.	_____	_____	_____
2.	_____	_____	_____
3.	_____	_____	_____
4.	_____	_____	_____
5.	_____	_____	_____

D. Sauce Review—Small Sauces

For the following small sauces identify the leading sauce that forms its base and list the main ingredients or garnish that distinguish them from the mother sauce.

Small Sauce	Ingredients Added	Mother Sauce
1. Mornay	_____	_____
2. Béarnaise	_____	_____
3. Bercy	_____	_____
4. Spanish	_____	_____
5. Poulette	_____	_____

Small Sauce	Ingredients Added	Mother Sauce
6. Bordelaise	_____	_____
7. Nantua	_____	_____
8. Normandy	_____	_____
9. Hungarian	_____	_____
10. Aurora	_____	_____
11. Chevreuil	_____	_____
12. Milanaise	_____	_____

E. True or False

For each question below circle either True or False to indicate the correct answer.

1. More roux is needed for dark sauces than for light ones.
   True   False

2. To avoid lumps in sauces, add hot stock to hot roux.
   True   False

3. After adding a liaison to a sauce, simmer for 5 minutes.
   True   False

4. Nappe is a term used to describe the consistency of sauce.
   True   False

5. The combination of water and cornstarch is called slurry.
   True   False

6. A velouté is a roux-based sauce.
   True   False

7. The definition of tempering is the gradual lowering of the temperature of a hot liquid by adding a cold liquid.
   True   False

8. A reduction method is sometimes used to thicken sauces.
   True   False

9. Compound sauces come from small sauces.
   True   False

10. Fish stock needs to simmer for one hour in order to impart flavor.
    True   False

F. Short Answer

Provide a short response that correctly answers each of the questions below.

1. List the 7 principles of stock making.

   a._____

b. _____

c. _____

d. _____

e. _____

f. _____

g. _____

2. Hollandaise Preparation:
   In the space below list the essential ingredients and describe in a step-by-step manner the preparation of hollandaise sauce, using the classical method. Exact quantities are important for this exercise, and each step should be numbered for revision purposes.

   Ingredients: *Procedure:*

   _____

   _____

   _____

   _____

   _____

   _____

   _____

   _____

   _____

3. Give five reasons why hollandaise sauce might separate.

   a. _____

   b. _____

   c. _____

   d. _____

   e. _____

G. Matching

Match each of the mother sauces in List A with the appropriate small sauce in List B. Each choice in List B can only be used once.

	List A		List B
_____	1. Espagnole	a.	Maltaise
_____	2. Hollandaise	b.	Creole
_____	3. Béchamel	c.	Chasseur
_____	4. Velouté	d.	Cardinal
		e.	Soubise

CHAPTER 11

SOUPS

Many of the skills learned in Stocks and Sauces are re-used in this chapter, but some new techniques must also be acquired. Some of these specialized techniques must be learned and practiced repeatedly in order to achieve successful results. The endless variation of soups that can result from experimentation with different raw materials makes this chapter especially interesting.

At the end of this chapter the student should be able to:

1. Describe the preparation of a variety of clear and thick soups.
2. Explain the appropriate service and garnishes for soups.

KEY TERMS

Broth   Chowder   Clearmeat
Consomme   Tomato concasse   Raft
Bisque   Onion brûlée   Render

TEST YOUR KNOWLEDGE

The practice sets provided below have been designed to test your comprehension of the information found in this chapter. It is recommended that you read the chapter completely before attempting these quesitons.

A. Terminology

Fill in the blank spaces with the correct term.

1. _____ The coagulated ingredients that rise to the surface during the clarification process of consomme.
2. _____ The burnt ingredient that is added to consomme to impart flavor and color of the soup.
3. _____ The melting and clarification of fat.

4. _____ A shellfish soup that was traditionally thickened with rice.

Fill in the blank spaces with the correct definition.

5. Clearmeat _____

6. Tomato concasse _____

7. Chowder _____

8. Broth _____

9. Consommé _____

B. Consommé Preparation Review I

The procedure for making consommé is time tested. List the essential ingredients and describe in a step-by-step manner the cooking procedure for consommé. Exact quantities are important for this exercise. Each step should be numbered for revision purposes.

Ingredients: *Procedure:*

_____

_____

_____

_____

_____

_____

_____

_____

C. Consommé Preparation Review II

Provide a reason for each of the following problems with consommé preparation.

1. Cloudy _____

2. Greasy _____

3. Lacks flavor _____

4. Lacks color _____

D. Cream Soup Preparation Review

Describe the procedure for making a cream soup using a fresh vegetable. List the essential ingredients, the quantities to be used, and suggest a garnish for the soup. Each step should be numbered for revision purposes.

Ingredients: *Procedure:*

_____

_____

_____

_____

_____

_____

_____

_____

_____

_____

_____

_____

_____

_____

_____

_____

E. Short Answer

Provide a short response that correctly answers each of the questions below.

1. List three steps that can be taken to prevent cream from curdling when it is added to cream soups?

   a. _____

   b. _____

   c. _____

2. List the 7 common categories of soups and provide 2 examples of type. Suggest an appropriate garnish for each soup.

Soup	*Example*	*Garnish*
a. _____	_____	_____
	_____	_____
b. _____	_____	_____
	_____	_____

c. _____ _____ _____
                    _____ _____

d. _____ _____ _____
                    _____ _____

e. _____ _____ _____
                    _____ _____

f. _____ _____ _____
                    _____ _____

g. _____ _____ _____
                    _____ _____

3. Compare and contrast the following soups. Explain what they have in common, and what makes them different from one another.

   a. Beef broth   Consommé

   _____
   _____
   _____
   _____

   b. Cream of mushroom   Lentil soup

   _____
   _____
   _____
   _____

   c. Gazpacho   Cold consommé

   _____
   _____
   _____
   _____

F. True or False

For each question below circle either True or False to indicate the correct answer.

1. A purée soup is usually more chunky than a cream soup.
   True   False

2. A crouton is bread that has been sautéed until crisp.
   True   False

3. Consomme should be stirred after the clearmeat is added.
   True   False

4. A broth is a consommé with vegetables added to it.
   True   False

5. Cream soups are thickened with a purée of vegetables which have been cooked in a stock.
   True   False

6. French onion soup has only one garnish; the croutons.
   True   False

7. Cold soups should be served at room temperature.
   True   False

8. Once a consommé is clouded it should be discarded.
   True   False

9. Cold soups need less seasoning than hot soups.
   True   False

10. A roux can be used as a thickener for cold soups.
    True   False.

CHAPTER 12

PRINCIPLES OF MEAT COOKERY

The meats offered on the menu are often the most popular items. It is therefore essential to have a full understanding of how heat transfer affects each cut of meat. This knowledge is the key to maximizing flavor for every cut of meat.

At the end of this chapter the student should be able to:

1. Explain the structure and composition of meats.
2. Describe meat inspection and grading practices.
3. Select meats for specific needs.
4. Explain the appropriate methods of meat storage.
5. Describe the preparation of meats before cooking.
6. Apply various cooking methods.

KEY TERMS

Primal cuts	Elastin	Vacuum packaging	Larding	Paillard
Subprimal cuts	Butcher	IMPS/NAMP	Fond	Medallion
Fabricated cuts	Dress	Freezer burn	Cutlet	Mignonette
Marbling	Fabricate	Marinating	Scallop	Noisette
Subcutaneous fat	Carve	Barding	Émincé	Chop

TEST YOUR KNOWLEDGE

The practice sets provided below have been designed to test your comprehension of the information found in this chapter. It is recommended that you read the chapter completely before attempting these questions.

A. Terminology

Fill in the blank spaces with the correct term.

1. _____ The primary divisions of muscle, bone, and connective tissue.

2. _____ The process of cutting cooked meat into individual portions.
3. _____ Otherwise known as silverskin, which will not break down during the cooking process.
4. _____ Streaks of fat which form in lean tissue.
5. _____ Covering the surface of meat with a thin layer of pork backfat.
6. _____ Another term for a medallion.
7. _____ The surface discoloration of foods that are directly exposed to below-freezing temperatures.
8. _____ The process of soaking meat in seasoned liquid to tenderize it.
9. _____ The abbreviated term for the publications covering meat specifications used by purchasers and purveyors.
10. _____ Inserting strips of fat into meat.

Fill in the blank spaces with the correct definition.

11. Noisette _____

12. Vacuum packaging _____

13. Butcher _____

14. Subprimal cuts _____

15. Dress _____

16. Fabricate _____

17. Subcutaneous fat _____

18. Fabricated cuts _____

19. Chop _____

20. Fond _____

B. True or False

For each question below circle True or False to indicate the correct answer.

1. Fresh meats should be stored at 35–40° F.
   True   False

2. "Green meats" are meats that are allowed to turn moldy.
   True   False

3. Braising and stewing are combination cooking methods.

True   False

4. The USDA stamp on whole carcasses of meat does not ensure their quality or tenderness.
   True   False

5. USDA choice meat is used in the finest restaurants and hotels.
   True   False

6. Yield grades are used for beef, lamb, and pork.
   True   False

7. Wet aging occurs in a vacuum package.
   True   False

8. During dry aging the meat may develop mold, which adds to the flavor of the meat.
   True   False

9. Under the correct conditions vacuum-packed meat can be held for 2 to 3 months.
   True   False

10. Still air freezing is the most common method of freezing meats in foodservice facilities.
    True   False.

C. Fill in the Blank

Fill in the blank with the response that correctly completes the statement.

1. Dry heat cooking methods are best used for _____ cuts of meat.
2. Once the meat is added to the sauce for stewing the dish is cooked at a _____ temperature for a _____ time.
3. Very rare meats should feel _____ and have a _____ color; however, well-cooked meats should feel _____ and have a _____ color.
4. Saute items are sometimes _____ before being placed in the pan.
5. Some _____ cooking occurs when a roast item is removed from the oven. Allowing the meat to rest will help the meat to _____ _____.

D. Matching

Match each of the stews in List A with the appropriate description in List B. Each choice in List B can only be used once.

List A	List B
_____ 1. Ragout	a. A spicy ragout of ground or diced meat with vegetables, peppers, and sometimes beans.
_____ 2. Goulash	b. A white stew usually made with white meat and garnished with onions and mushrooms.
_____ 3. Blanquette	c. A brown ragout made with root vegetables and lamb.
_____ 4. Fricassee	d. A general term that refers to stews.
_____ 5. Navarin	e. A Hungarian beef stew made with onions and paprika and garnished with potatoes.
	f. A white stew in which the meat is blanched and added to the sauce to finish the cooking process. This stew is finished with a liaison of cream and egg yolks.

E. Cooking Methods

Provide a short response that correctly answers each of the questions below.

Briefly describe each of the following methods of cooking and provide an example of a cut of meat used in each method.

Cooking Method	Description	Example
Grilling	_____	_____
Roasting	_____	_____
Sauteing	_____	_____
Pan-frying	_____	_____
Simmering	_____	_____
Braising	_____	_____
Stewing	_____	_____

CHAPTER 13

BEEF

Beef is the most popular meat among Americans. This chapter explains the different cuts of beef and their preparation for cooking.

At the end of this chapter the student should be able to:

1. Identify the primal, subprimal, and fabricated cuts of beef.
2. Explain the basic butchering procedures.
3. Identify the appropriate cooking methods for several common cuts of beef.

KEY TERMS

Chuck	Short plate	Chateaubriand	Round
Brisket	Short loin	Flank	
Shank	Porterhouse	Round	
Rib	Tenderloin	Steamship round	

TEST YOUR KNOWLEDGE

The practice sets provided below have been designed to test your comprehension of the information found in this chapter. It is recommended that you read the chapter completely before attempting these questions.

A. Terminology

Fill in the blank spaces with the correct term.

1. _____ Compared to T-bone steaks, these steaks have a larger portion of tenderloin.
2. _____ Contains rib bones and cartilage and produces meaty ribs and skirt steak.
3. _____ The shoulder cut of beef which is made up of a portion of the backbone, 5 rib bones, and portions of the blade and arm bones.

4. _____ The beef round rump with the shank partially removed which is used for roasting.

5. _____ The hind leg of the animal which can weigh up to 200 pounds.

6. _____ The largest, thickest portion of the tenderloin.

7. _____ The meat from this cut is used to clarify and add flavor to consommés due to its high collagen content.

Fill in the blank spaces with the correct definition.

8. Tenderloin _____

9. Offal _____

10. Flank _____

11. Short loin _____

12. Rib _____

13. Brisket _____

B. Primal Cuts of Beef

Identify the primal cuts of beef indicated in the following diagram and write their names in the spaces provided.

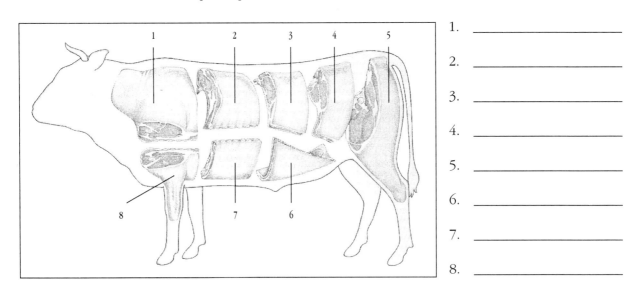

1. _____
2. _____
3. _____
4. _____
5. _____
6. _____
7. _____
8. _____

C. Cuts from the Round

Name the 5 subprimal/fabricated cuts from the round and name the most appropriate cooking process or use for each cut.

	Subprimal/Fabricated Cut	Cooking Process/Use
1.	_____	_____
2.	_____	_____
3.	_____	_____
4.	_____	_____
5.	_____	_____

D. Cuts of Beef and Applied Cooking Methods

Name the cooking method applied to the main ingredient in each of the following beef dishes. Also, identify a subprimal and a primal cut of meat from which the main ingredient is taken.

Name of Dish	Cooking Method	Subprimal/ Fabricated Cut	Primal Cut
1. Meatloaf	_____	_____	_____
2. Beef Wellington	_____	_____	_____
3. Chateaubriand	_____	_____	_____
4. T-bone steak	_____	_____	_____
5. Minute steak	_____	_____	_____
6. London broil	_____	_____	_____
7. Beef roulade	_____	_____	_____
8. Prime rib	_____	_____	_____
9. Corned beef	_____	_____	_____
10. Beef fajitas	_____	_____	_____

E. Multiple Choice

For each question below, choose the one response that correctly answers the question.

1. The outside round and the eye of the round together are called the:
   a. top round
   b. bottom round
   c. steamship round
   d. primal round

2. A carcass of beef weighs:
   a. between 600 and 950 pounds
   b. up to 1,000 pounds
   c. from 500 to more than 800 pounds
   d. between 400 and 600 pounds
3. The three fabricated cuts from the tenderloin are:
   a. porterhouse steak, tournedos, and chateaubriand
   b. butt tenderloin, filet mignon, and tournedos
   c. chateaubriand, short loin, and loin eye
   d. tournedos, chateaubriand, and filet mignon
4. "Butterflying" is a preparation technique which:
   a. makes the cut of meat thinner
   b. makes the meat more tender
   c. improves the flavor of the meat
   d. improves the appearance of the meat

F. True or False

For each question below circle either True or False to indicate the correct answer.

1. The hanging tenderloin is part of the flank.
   True   False

2. The meat from the chuck is less flavorful than meat from the tenderloin.
   True   False

3. A porterhouse steak is a fabricated cut from the tenderloin.
   True   False

4. Prime rib of beef refers to the quality USDA grade.
   True   False

5. The subprimal and fabricated cuts from the short loin are the most tender and expensive cuts of beef.
   True   False

6. The subprimals and fabricated cuts from the sirloin are not as tender as those from the strip loin.
   True   False

7. The short loin can be cut across to produce porterhouse, T-bone and club steaks.
   True   False

8. Pastrami is made from the meat in the short plate.
   True   False

G. Matching

Match each of the primal cuts in List A with the appropriate description in List B. Each choice in List B can only be used once.

	List A
_____	1. Rib
_____	2. Chuck
_____	3. Short Loin
_____	4. Flank

List B

a. Produces the boneless strip loin, which can be roasted whole or cut into steaks

b. This cut is located in the hindquarter between the short loin and the round.

c. The eye of this cut is well exercised, quite tender, and contains large quantities of marbling. It is suitable for roasting.

d. The animal constantly uses the muscle in this primal cut, therefore it is tough, contains high levels of connective tissue, and is very flavorful.

e. This primal cut produces the hanging tenderloin which is very tender and can be cooked by any method.

CHAPTER 14

VEAL

Veal is a most delicately flavored meat and requires special care during cooking. A knowledge of the different muscles in this young animal is essential.

At the end of this chapter the student should be able to:

1. Identify the primal, subprimal and fabricated cuts of veal.
2. Explain the basic butchering procedures.
3. Identify the appropriate cooking methods for several common cuts of veal.

KEY TERMS

Veal	Breast
Calf	Hotel rack
Shoulder	Loin
Foreshank	Sweetbreads

TEST YOUR KNOWLEDGE

The practice sets provided below have been designed to test your comprehension of the information found in this chapter. It is recommended that you read the chapter completely before attempting these questions.

A. Terminology

Fill in the blank spaces with the correct term.

1. _____ This primal cut is located behind the primal rib and consists of the loin eye muscle on top of the rib bones and the tenderloin under them.
2. _____ This cut is high in cartilage, fat, and connective tissue and therefore makes a very flavorful stew.
3. _____ The meat of calves under the age of nine months.

4. _____ The primal cut that is made up of 4 rib bones and portions of the backbone, blade, and arms.

Fill in the blank spaces with the correct definition.

5. Sweetbreads _____

6. Foreshank _____

7. Hotel rack _____

8. Calf _____

B. Primal Cuts of Veal

Identify the primal cuts of veal indicated in the following diagram and write their names in the spaces provided.

1. _____

2. _____

3. _____

4. _____

5. _____

C. Cuts of Veal and Applied Cooking Methods

Name the cooking method applied to the main ingredient in each of the following dishes. Also, identify a subprimal and a primal cut of meat from which the main ingredient is taken.

Name of Dish	Cooking Method	Subprimal/ Fabricated Cut	Primal Cut
1. Osso bucco	_____	_____	_____
2. Veal cutlets	_____	_____	_____
3. Veal fricassee	_____	_____	_____
4. Veal marsala	_____	_____	_____
5. Veal scallopini	_____	_____	_____
6. Veal medallions with green peppercorn sauce	_____	_____	_____

Name of Dish	Cooking Method	Subprimal/ Fabricated Cut	Primal Cut
7. Veal tenderloin with garlic and herbs	_____	_____	_____
8. Stuffed veal breast	_____	_____	_____
9. Stuffed veal scallops	_____	_____	_____
10. Blanquette of veal	_____	_____	_____

D. Short Answer

Provide a short response that correctly answers each of the questions below.

1. Briefly describe the 8 basic steps to be followed when boning a leg of veal, beginning with:

   a. <u>Remove the shank</u>_____

   b. _____

   c. _____

   d. _____

   e. _____

   f. _____

   g. _____

   h. _____

2. Name the 6 muscles in the leg of veal.

   a. _____

   b. _____

   c. _____

   d. _____

   e. _____

   f. _____

3. Name the 3 subprimal cuts from the rib and 3 from the loin and provide a menu example of each cut.

Primal Cut	Subprimal/Fabricated Cut	Menu Example
a. Rib	_____	_____
b. Rib	_____	_____
c. Rib	_____	_____
a. Loin	_____	_____
b. Loin	_____	_____
c. Loin	_____	_____

4. Compare and contrast formula-fed veal with free-range veal. Discuss the advantages and disadvantages of each.

_____

_____

_____

_____

_____

_____

_____

E. Matching

Match the primal cuts in List A with the appropriate definitions in List B. Each choice in List B can only be used once.

List A

_____ 1. Leg

_____ 2. Shoulder

_____ 3. Foreshank and Breast

_____ 4. Loin

_____ 5. Rib

List B

a. A cut of veal similar to the chuck in beef.

b. A primal cut of veal which is located just below the shoulder and rib section in the front of the carcass.

c. The primal cut that produces the short tenderloin.

d. The bones in this cut are still soft, due to the immaturity of the animal.

e. The primal cut that yields the most tender meat.

f. Made up of portions of the backbone, tail bone, hip bone, aitch bone, round bone, and shank.

F. True or False

For each question below circle either True or False to indicate the correct answer.

1. Veal scallops are taken from large pieces of veal and are cut on the bias, across the grain of the meat.
   True   False

2. Veal flesh begins to change color when the animal consumes iron in its food.
   True   False

3. Sweetbreads are pressed to remove the impurities.
   True   False

4. Veal émincé are cut with the grain, from small pieces of meat.
   True   False

5. Veal scallops are pounded in order to make them more tender.
   True   False

6. Sweetbreads become larger as the animal ages.
   True   False

7. Veal liver has a more delicate flavor than beef liver.
   True   False

8. The hindshank and foreshank of veal are prepared and cooked in the same manner.
   True   False

CHAPTER 15

LAMB

Lamb is a versatile meat that can be cooked by almost any method. This chapter outlines the various methods of preparing lamb and its accompanying sauces.

At the end of this chapter the student should be able to:

1. Identify the primal, subprimal, and fabricated cuts of lamb.
2. Explain the basic butchering procedures.
3. Identify the appropriate cooking methods for several common cuts of lamb.

KEY TERMS

Lamb
Mutton
French
Rack
Bracelet

TEST YOUR KNOWLEDGE

The practice sets provided below have been designed to test your comprehension of the information found in this chapter. It is recommended that you read the chapter completely before attempting these questions.

A. Terminology

Fill in the blank spaces with the correct definition.

1. Rack   _____

2. Mutton   _____

3. Bracelet   _____

Fill in the blank spaces with the correct term.

4. _____ The meat of sheep slaughtered under the age of one year.

5. _____ A method of trimming racks or chops in which the excess fat is removed and the rib bones are cleaned.

B. Primal Cuts of Lamb

Identify the primal cuts of lamb indicated in the following diagram and write their names in the spaces provided below.

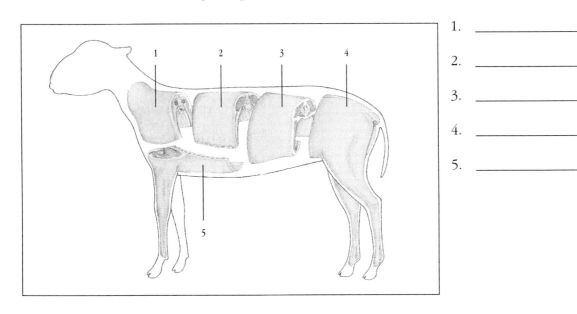

1. _____

2. _____

3. _____

4. _____

5. _____

C. Subprimal or Fabricated Cuts

For each primal cut named above, name two subprimal cuts and an appropriate cooking method for each of these cuts.

Primal Cut	Subprimal/Fabricated Cut	Cooking Methods
1.	a. _____	_____
	b. _____	_____
2.	a. _____	_____
	b. _____	_____
3.	a. _____	_____
	b. _____	_____
4.	a. _____	_____
	b. _____	_____
5.	a. _____	_____
	b. _____	_____

D. Cuts of Lamb and Applied Cooking Methods

Name the cooking method applied to the main ingredient in each of the following lamb dishes. Also, identify a subprimal and a primal cut of meat from which the main ingredient is taken.

Name of Dish	Cooking Method	Subprimal/ Fabricated Cut	Primal Cut
1. Lamb kebabs	_____	_____	_____
2. Lamb curry	_____	_____	_____
3. Noisettes of lamb with roasted garlic sauce	_____	_____	_____
4. Lamb navarin	_____	_____	_____
5. Broiled lamb with mustard and hazelnut crust	_____	_____	_____

E. Short Answer

Provide a short response that correctly answers the questions below.

1. Briefly describe the 6 basic steps to be followed when frenching a rack of lamb.

   a. _____

   b. _____

   c. _____

   d. _____

   e. _____

   f. _____

2. Briefly describe the 4 basic steps to be followed when trimming a leg of lamb for roasting/grilling.

   a. _____

   b. _____

   c. _____

   d. _____

3. Briefly describe the 8 basic steps to be followed when preparing a loin of lamb for roasting.

a. _____

b. _____

c. _____

d. _____

e. _____

f. _____

g. _____

h. _____

i. _____

F. True or False

For each question below circle either True or False to indicate the correct answer.

1. The lamb carcass is classified into two parts—the hindquarter and the fore-quarter.
   True   False

2. The term "spring lamb" applies to animals that are born between February and May.
   True   False

3. The primal cuts of both veal and lamb are broken down into bilateral halves.
   True   False

4. The primal leg of lamb is rarely left whole.
   True   False

5. The leg of lamb can be broken down to produce steaks.
   True   False

6. The chine bone runs through the loin of lamb.
   True   False

7. The "fell" refers to thin layer of connective tissue on the outside of the loin of lamb.
   True   False

8. Denver ribs are ribs that are cut from the breast of lamb.
   True   False

CHAPTER 16

PORK

Pork has taken on a new popularity in recent times in the United States. This chapter describes the many different preparations for this versatile flavorsome meat.

At the end of this chapter the student should be able to:

1. Identify the primal, subprimal, and fabricated cuts of pork.
2. Explain the basic butchering procedures.
3. Identify the appropriate cooking methods for several cuts of pork.

KEY TERMS

Pork   Spareribs
Picnic shoulder   Backribs
Boston butt   Ham
Belly

TEST YOUR KNOWLEDGE

The practice sets provided below have been designed to test your comprehension of the information found in this chapter. It is recommended that you read the chapter completely before attempting these questions.

A. Terminology

Fill in the spaces with the correct definition.

1. Belly   _____

2. Pork   _____

3. Ham   _____

4. Backribs   _____

Fill in the spaces with the correct term.

5. _____ The ribs that are taken from the belly.

6. _____ Another term for the primal shoulder which contains the arm and shank bones and has a relatively high ratio of bone to lean meat.

7. _____ The square cut located just above the primal shoulder also known as a cottage ham.

B. Primal Cuts of Pork

Identify the primal cuts of pork indicated in the following diagram and write their names in the spaces provided below.

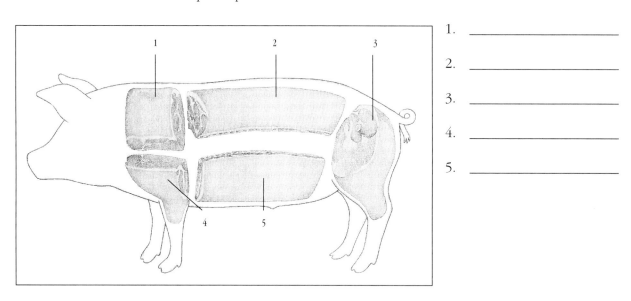

1. _____

2. _____

3. _____

4. _____

5. _____

C. Subprimal or Fabricated Cuts

For each primal cut named above, name a subprimal cut and an appropriate cooking method. Indicate in the appropriate columns(s) whether these cuts are usually smoked or fresh (or both).

Primal Cut	Subprimal/ Fabricated Cut	Cooking Methods	Cured & Smoked	Fresh
1. _____	_____	_____	____	____
2. _____	_____	_____	____	____
3. _____	_____	_____	____	____
4. _____	_____	_____	____	____
5. _____	_____	_____	____	____

Example:

Fresh ham	Hock	Braise		X

D. Cuts of Pork and Applied Cooking Methods

Name the cooking method applied to the main ingredient in each of the following recipes. Also identify a subprimal and a primal cut of meat from which the main ingredient is taken.

Name of Dish	Cooking Method	Subprimal/ Fabricated Cut	Primal Cut
1. Stuffed pork chops	_____	_____	_____
2. Sautéed pork medallions with red pepper and citrus	_____	_____	_____
3. Breakfast bacon	_____	_____	_____
4. Choucroute	_____	_____	_____
5. Carolina barbecue ribs	_____	_____	_____
6. Barbecue spare ribs	_____	_____	_____
7. Roast pork with apricots and almonds	_____	_____	_____
8. Roast pork	_____	_____	_____

E. Short Answer

Provide a short response that correctly answers the questions below.

1. Briefly describe the three basic steps to be followed when boning a pork loin.

   a. _____

   b. _____

   c. _____

2. Name 6 fabricated cuts that are most often smoked and cured.

   a. _____

   b. _____

   c. _____

   d. _____

   e. _____

   f. _____

F. Matching

Match the primal cuts in List A with the appropriate definitions in List B. Each choice in List B can only be used once.

List A

_____ 1. Boston butt

_____ 2. Shoulder

_____ 3. Belly

_____ 4. Loin

_____ 5. Fresh ham

List B

a. A primal cut that is very fatty with strips of lean meat.

b. The primal cut from which the most tender portion of pork is taken.

c. A primal cut which contains large muscles and relatively small amounts of connective tissue. It may be smoked and cured or cooked fresh.

d. A primal cut with a good percentage of fat to lean meat—ideal when a solid piece of pork is required for a recipe.

e. A single, very tender eye muscle that can be braised/roasted/sautéed.

f. One of the toughest cuts of pork. It has a relatively high ratio of bone to lean meat, is relatively inexpensive and widely available.

G. True or False

For each question below circle either True or False to indicate the correct answer.

1. The Boston butt is located in the hindquarter.
   True   False

2. Pork is unique because the ribs and loin are considered one primal cut.
   True   False

3. The term "meat packing" originated in colonial times when pork was packed into barrels for shipment abroad.
   True   False

4. The foreshank is also known as the ham hock.
   True   False

5. Center-cut pork chops are chops that are split open to form a pocket.
   True   False

6. The belly is used to make Canadian bacon.
   True   False

7. Backfat is the layer of fat between the skin and the lean muscle of the pork loin.
   True   False

8. The two primal cuts that produce ribs are the loin and the belly.
   True   False

9. Hogs are bred to produce short loins.
   True   False

10. Picnic ham is made from the hog's hind leg.
    True   False

CHAPTER 17

POULTRY

Poultry is perhaps the most versatile and least expensive main dish food. This chapter discusses the many different types of poultry, the safety precautions to be taken so that food-borne illness may be avoided, and the cooking methods applied to poultry.

At the end of this chapter the student should be able to:

1. Describe the structure and composition of poultry.
2. Identify various kinds and classes of poultry.
3. Explain poultry inspection and grading practices.
4. Select poultry for specific needs.
5. Explain the appropriate methods of poultry storage.
6. Describe the preparation of poultry before cooking.
7. Apply various cooking methods.

KEY TERMS

Game hen	Suprême
Capon	A point
Giblets	Trussing
Foie gras	

TEST YOUR KNOWLEDGE

The practice sets provided below have been designed to test your comprehension of the information found in this chapter. It is recommended that you read the chapter completely before attempting these questions.

A. Terminology

Fill in the spaces with the correct definition.

1. Giblets _____

2. Trussing   _____

3. Capon   _____

4. Suprême   _____

Fill in the spaces with the correct term.

5. _____ The French term for the degree of doneness, i.e., when the juices run clear from poultry.

6. _____ The young immature offspring of a Cornish chicken or of a Cornish chicken and a White Rock chicken.

7. _____ The enlarged liver of a duck or goose.

B. Short Answer

Provide a short response that correctly answers each of the questions below.

1. List 5 important guidelines for stuffing poultry.

   a. _____

   b. _____

   c. _____

   d. _____

   e. _____

2. Name one similarity and one major difference between poultry and red meats.

   Similarity: _____

   _____

   Difference: _____

   _____

3. Poultry is a highly perishable product and improper storage can lead to food poisoning. Discuss the guidelines for storing poultry products under the following headings.
*Include *exact* temperatures and times in this answer.

   Storage under refrigeration: _____

   _____

   Freezing: _____

   _____

Thawing: _____

_____

Reheating: _____

4. List 5 differences between the rearing and sale of free-range chicken compared to traditionally reared chicken.

   a. _____

   b. _____

   c. _____

   d. _____

   e. _____

5. What are the six categories of poultry?

   a. _____

   b. _____

   c. _____

   d. _____

   e. _____

   f. _____

6. For each of the following cooking methods, give a recipe example and accompaniment for the poultry item.

Cooking Method	Recipe Example	Accompaniment
Sauté	_____	_____
Pan-fry	_____	_____
Simmer/Poach	_____	_____
Braise/Stew	_____	_____

7. Describe 5 ways to prevent cross-contamination when handling poultry.

   a. _____

   b. _____

   c. _____

   d. _____

   e. _____

8. Describe the 6 steps for portioning poultry into 8 pieces.

a. _____

b. _____

c. _____

d. _____

e. _____

f. _____

C. Matching

Match each of the terms in List A with the appropriate letter definition in List B. Each choice in List B can only be used once.

List A

_____ 1. Hen/stewing

_____ 2. Broiler/fryer

_____ 3. Roaster

_____ 4. Capon

_____ 5. Game hen

List B

a. Young tender meat, smooth skin, breastbone less flexible than a broiler's (3-5 months).

b. Mature female, less tender meat, nonflexible breastbone (over 10 months).

c. Young immature offspring of Cornish chicken, very flavorful (5-6 weeks).

d. Rich, tender dark meat with large amounts of fat, soft windpipe (6 months or less).

e. Young with soft, smooth skin, lean with flexible breastbone (13 weeks).

f. Surgically castrated male, tender meat, smooth skin, high proportion of light to dark meat, relatively high fat content (under 8 months).

D. Fill in the Blank

Fill in the blank provided with the response that correctly completes the statement.

1. The color difference between the legs and wings of chicken and turkey is due to a higher concentration of the _____ called _____ in the tissue.
2. The internal temperature of fully cooked poultry should be between _____ and _____.
3. The most commonly used duck in foodservice operations is a _____. Its meat is different from chicken in two ways: the flesh is _____ and has large amounts of _____.
4. Chicken is often marinated in a mixture of _____.

A common example of a chicken marinade is _____ sauce.

E. Multiple Choice

For each question below, choose one response that correctly answers the question.

1. Poultry should be refrigerated between:
   a. 30–35°F
   b. 33–36°F
   c. 32–34°F
   d. 30–38°F

2. Which of the following groups do not fall into the "poultry" category?
   a. chicken, duck, pigeon
   b. duck, pheasant, goose
   c. pigeon, guineas, chicken
   d. none of the above

3. The poultry that is sold in wholesale or retail outlets carries the USDA Grade
   a. A
   b. C
   c. B
   d. all of the above

F. True or False

For each question below circle either True or False to indicate the correct answer.

1. Poultry fat has a higher melting point than other animal fats.
   True   False

2. Duck and goose must be roasted at a higher temperature in order to render as much fat from the skin as possible.
   True   False

3. Myoglobin is a protein that stores oxygen.
   True   False

4. The longer chicken is left in a marinade, the better the flavor.
   True   False

5. Dark meat takes less time to cook than light meat.
   True   False

6. Poultry should not be frozen below -18C/0F.
   True   False

7. The skin color of poultry is partly affected by the amount of sunlight it is exposed to.
   True   False

8. Quality USDA grades do not reflect the tenderness of poultry.
   True   False

9. Older male birds have more flavor than female birds.
   True   False

10. When foie gras is overcooked it becomes tough.
    True   False

11. A young pigeon is called a yearling.
    True   False

12. The gizzard is a term used to describe the chicken's neck.
    True   False

CHAPTER 18

GAME

Game has become more popular and available in the United States since farm-raising techniques have been perfected. This chapter outlines the many different types of game and discusses the most appropriate cooking methods for them.

At the end of this chapter the student should be able to:

1. Identify a variety of game.
2. Describe game inspection practices.
3. Select game for specific needs.
4. Explain appropriate methods of game storage.
5. Describe the preparation of game before cooking.
6. Apply various cooking methods.

KEY TERMS

Game   Buffalo
Venison   Hanging

TEST YOUR KNOWLEDGE

The practice sets provided below have been designed to test your comprehension of the information found in this chapter. It is recommended that you read the chapter completely before attempting these questions.

A. Terminology

Fill in the spaces with the correct term.

1. _____ Animals that are hunted for sport or food.

2. _____ The process used to tenderize the flesh and strengthen the flavor of game.

Fill in the spaces with the correct definition.

3. Venison _____

4. Buffalo _____

B. Short Answer

Provide a short response that correctly answers the questions below.

1. List 3 uses for tougher cuts of game.

   a. _____

   b. _____

   c. _____

2. Explain the process and purpose for hanging wild game.

   Process: _____

   _____

   _____

   _____

   Purpose:_____

   _____

3. Describe the origins and makeup of Beefalo.

   _____

   _____

   _____

   _____

4. Describe the guidelines for refrigeration and freezing of game.

   _____

   _____

   _____

   _____

C. Multiple Choice

For each question below, choose the one response that correctly answers the question.

1. Which of the following cannot be categorized as furred game?
   a. antelope
   b. pheasant
   c. bison
   d. rabbit

2. Due to the lean nature of game birds they are barded and cooked:
   a. medium
   b. rare
   c. medium rare
   d. well done

3. Which one of the following is *not* a member of the deer family?
   a. elk
   b. bison
   c. mule deer
   d. moose
4. Feathered game include:
   a. pheasant, quail, woodcock
   b. partridge, pheasant, pigeon
   c. turkey, lark, squab
   d. guinea, goose, duck
5. Quail weighs approximately:
   a. 10–12 ounces
   b. 1–2 pounds
   c. 4–5 pounds
   d. none of the above
6. The most popular game bird is:
   a. quail
   b. partridge
   c. pheasant
   d. woodcock

D. *True or False*

For each question below circle either True or False to indicate the correct answer.

1. Most farmed deer is not slaughtered or processed in the slaughterhouse.
   True   False

2. Wild antelope, venison, and rabbit are not subject to inspection under federal law.
   True   False

3. A mature boar (3-4 years old) has a better flavor than a younger animal.
   True   False

4. Wild game birds can be purchased by request from most butchers.
   True   False

5. Wild boar is closely related to the domestic pig.
   True   False

6. Game is higher in fat and vitamins than most other meats.
   True   False

7. Venison is very moist due the marbling through the tissue.
   True   False

8. Large game animals are usually sold in primal portions.
   True   False

9. Furred game meat has a finer grain than other meats.
   True   False

10. The aroma, texture, and flavor of game is affected by the lifestyle of the animal.
    True   False

CHAPTER 19

FISH AND SHELLFISH

Fish and shellfish have always been an important food source, but they have become increasingly popular in recent years. The development of fish farms has improved the availability and quality of seafood. A knowledge of the numerous varieties of fish, their seasonability, perishability, flavor characteristics, and the best preparation techniques is essential in the modern kitchen.

After studying this chapter the student should be able to:

1. Identify the structure and composition of fish and shellfish.
2. Identify a variety of fish and shellfish.
3. Purchase fish and shellfish appropriate for the needs of the establishment.
4. Store fish and shellfish properly.
5. Prepare fish and shellfish for cooking.
6. Apply various appropriate cooking methods to fish and shellfish.

KEY TERMS

Round fish
Fillet
Crustaceans
Tranche
Dressed

Pan-dressed
Mollusks
Wheel or center cut
Drawn

Flatfish
Steak
Aquafarming
En papillote

TEST YOUR KNOWLEDGE

The practice sets provided below have been designed to test your comprehension of the information found in this chapter. It is recommended that you read the chapter completely before attempting these questions.

A. Terminology

Fill in the blank spaces with the correct term.

1. _____ A method of steaming achieved by wrapping the fish or shellfish in parchment paper with other flavoring ingredients and baking in the oven.

2. _____ Shellfish with soft, unsegmented bodies with no internal skeleton.

3. _____ The business, science, and practice of raising large quantities of fish and shellfish in tanks, ponds, or ocean pens.

4. _____ The viscera and gills are removed, the fish scaled and fins and tails trimmed. The heads of small fish may remain, and then the fish is pan-fried.

5. _____ These swim in a vertical position and have eyes on both sides of their heads.

6. _____ Shellfish with a hard outer skeleton or shell and jointed appendages.

7. _____ Usually from a large roundfish, it is a cross-section slice with a small portion of the backbone attached.

8. _____ The most common way of purchasing fish; viscera is removed.

Fill in the blank spaces with the correct definition.

9. Fillet _____

10. Tranche _____

11. Dressed _____

12. Flat fish _____

13. Wheel or center cut _____

B. Multiple Choice

For each question below, choose the one response that correctly answers the question.

1. To maintain optimum freshness, fish and shellfish should be stored at what temperature?
   a. 40 degrees F.
   b. 30–34 degrees F.
   c. 40–45 degrees F.
   d. 38–40 degrees F.

2. Fish are graded:
   a. USDA Prime, Choice, Select, or Utility
   b. Type 1, Type 2, Type 3
   c. Premium, Commercial Grade, Cutter/Canner
   d. USDC A, B, or C

3. Clams, mussels, and oysters should be stored:
   a. at 36 degrees F.
   b. on ice and in refrigeration
   c. in boxes or net bags
   d. at 20 % humidity

4. Univalves and bivalves are both examples of:
   a. mollusks
   b. cephalopods
   c. clams
   d. crustaceans

5. The "universal" meaning of *prawn* refers to a:
   a. shrimp sautéed in garlic and butter
   b. all shrimp, freshwater or marine variety
   c. shrimp from the Gulf of Mexico
   d. freshwater variety of shrimp only

6. In terms of the market forms of fish, *dressed* refers to:
   a. viscera removed
   b. viscera, gills, fins, and scales removed
   c. as caught, intact
   d. viscera, fins, and gills removed, scaled, and tail trimmed

7. The most important commercial variety of salmon is:
   a. Atlantic
   b. Pacific
   c. Chinook
   d. King

8. Which type of sole cannot be caught off the coastline of the United States?
   a. Lemon
   b. English
   c. Petrale
   d. Dover

9. Mackerel, wahoo, herring, sardines, and salmon have similar characteristics in that:
   a. the color of their flesh is the same
   b. they all migrate
   c. their flesh is moderate-highly oily
   d. their geographic availability is the same

10. All clams are examples of:
    a. cephalopods
    b. crustaceans
    c. univalves
    d. bivalves

11. The best-selling fish in America is:
    a. Atlantic salmon
    b. lemon sole
    c. cod
    d. ahi tuna

12. When cooking fish fillets with the skin on, what can be done to prevent the fillet from curling?
    a. Cook fillet at a high temperature, short time
    b. Cook fillet at a low temperature, longer time
    c. Score the skin of the fish before cooking
    d. Flatten the fillet by weighing down with a semi-heavy object during cooking

C. Market Forms of Fish

Identify the market forms indicated in the following diagram and write their names in the spaces provided below.

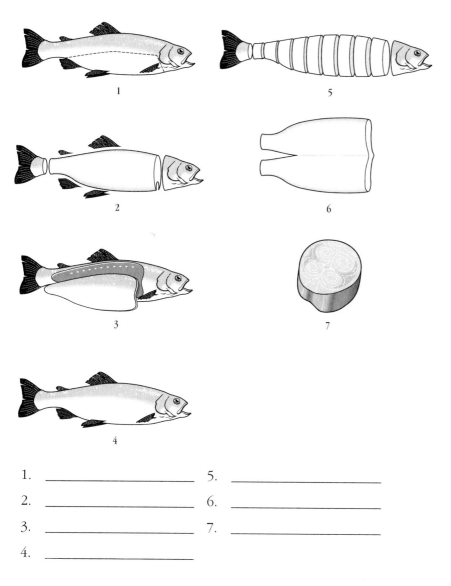

1. _____   5. _____

2. _____   6. _____

3. _____   7. _____

4. _____

D. Short Answer

Provide a short response that correctly answers each of the questions below.

1. Give two reasons why fish fillets and steaks are the best market forms to bake.

   a. _____

   b. _____

2. List the four guidelines for determining the doneness of fish and shellfish.

   a. _____

   b. _____

   c. _____

   d. _____

3. List four cooking methods that would be appropriate for preparing a tranche of salmon.

   a. _____

   b. _____

   c. _____

   d. _____

4. List two oily and 2 lean fish that grill well.

   oily   **lean**

   a. _____   c. _____

   b. _____   d. _____

5. Name four types of shellfish good for sautéing.

   a. _____   c. _____

   b. _____   d. _____

6. List three dishes that exemplify why shellfish are good for baking.

   a. _____

   b. _____

   c. _____

7. Explain two reasons why combination cooking methods are not traditionally used to prepare fish and shellfish.

   a. _____

   b. _____

8. List 4 of the 7 quality points used to determine the freshness of fish.

   a. _____   c. _____

   b. _____   d. _____

E. True or False

For each question below circle either True or False to indicate the correct answer.

1. All fish are eligible for grading.
   True   False

2. Fish and shellfish inspections are mandatory.
   True   False

3. A lobster is an example of a crustacean.
   True   False

4. Fatty fish are especially good for baking.
   True   False

5. The only difference between Maine lobsters and spiny lobsters is the geographic location where they're caught.
   True   False

6. Atlantic hard-shell clams are also known as geoducks.
   True   False

7. Fillet of halibut is a good fish to pan-fry.
   True   False

8. Cooking fish or shellfish en papillote is an example of baking.
   True   False

9. Shellfish has as much cholesterol as lamb.
   True   False

10. A cuisson is a classic accompaniment to poached salmon.
    True   False

CHAPTER 20

CHARCUTERIE

Over the years, charcuterie has developed from pork preparations of pâtés, terrines, and galantines, to include game, poultry, fish, shellfish, and even vegetables. The increased versatility of these items on menus has reflected the art and science of such preparations.

At the end of this chapter the student should be able to:

1. Explain the procedure of preparing a variety of forcemeats.
2. Assemble and cook a variety of pâtés, terrines, and sausages.
3. Compare and contrast the proper methods for salting, brining, curing, and smoking meats and fish.
4. Identify several cured pork products.

KEY TERMS

Country-style forcemeat	Pâté en croûte	Panada
Basic forcemeat	Aspic jelly	Mousseline forcemeat
Brawns	Rillettes	Curing salt
Confit	Quenelles	Ballottine
Pâté	Sausage	Terrine
Brine	Galantine	Smoking

TEST YOUR KNOWLEDGE

The practice sets provided below have been designed to test your comprehension of the information found in this chapter. It is recommended that you read this chapter completely before attempting these questions.

A. Terminology

Fill in the blank spaces with the correct term.

1. _____ Hot or cold; salt curing, brining or not, this preparation imparts distinctive flavor to the food.

2. _____ A "marinade" with approximately 20% salinity, sugar, herbs, and sometimes nitrites.

3. _____ Forcemeats stuffed into casings.

4. _____ The most versatile of all forcemeats, it is smoother and more refined than country-style.

5. _____ Preserved pork and fatty poultry that has been seasoned and slow cooked in large amounts of its own fat. Cooked until falling off the bone, the meat is then mashed and pressed into crocks or terrines with additional fat.

6. _____ A preparation more basic than pâté, it consists of coarsely ground and highly seasoned meats baked in an earthenware mold and always served cold.

7. _____ Preserved pork and fatty poultry that is often lightly salt-cured before being cooked in large amounts of its own fat; usually served hot.

8. _____ Small dumpling-shaped portions of a mousseline forcemeat poached in an appropriately flavored stock.

9. _____ An aspic terrine made from simmered meats packed into a terrine and covered with aspic.

Fill in the blank spaces with the correct definition.

10. Country-style forcemeat _____

11. Curing salt _____

12. Galantine _____

13. Pâté en croûte _____

14. Aspic jelly _____

15. Pâté _____

_____

16. Mousseline forcemeat _____

_____

17. Ballottine _____

_____

18. Panada _____

B. Short Answer

Provide a short response that correctly answers each of the questions below.

1. Name three kinds of forcemeat can be used to make a pâté en croûte.

   a. _____

   b. _____

   c. _____

2. If a forcemeat will not emulsify in a warm kitchen, what can be done?

   _____

3. Compare and contrast a galantine and a ballottine.

   galantine   **ballottine**

   a. _____   _____

   b. _____   _____

   c. _____   _____

   d. _____   _____

   e. _____   _____

   f. _____

4. What are three steps one can take to ensure proper emulsification of a forcemeat?

   a. _____

   b. _____

   c. _____

5. List five reasons for using an aspic jelly.

   a. _____

   b. _____

   c. _____

   d. _____

   e. _____

C. Multiple Choice

For each question below, choose the one response that correctly answers the question.

1. When making a forcemeat, ingredient as well as equipment temperatures should be kept at what temperature throughout preparation?
   a. below 40 degrees F.
   b. as cold as possible
   c. room temperature, but not to exceed 60 degrees F.
   d. 42–45 degrees F.

2. Which of the following is *NOT* true about salt curing? It:
   a. inhibits bacterial growth
   b. dehydrates the food
   c. is quick and easy
   d. can take the place of cooking

3. Meat-based galantines, terrines, and pâtés en croûte should be cooked to an internal temperature of:
   a. 140 degrees F.
   b. 125 degrees F.
   c. 150 degrees F.
   d. 160 degrees F.

4. When meats are cold smoked, what process is usually performed prior to the smoking?
   a. salt-curing and brining
   b. trimming
   c. barding
   d. marinated

5. What gives ham, bacon, and other smoked meats their pink color?
   a. red dye #7 is added to the curing process
   b. the meat is cooked to a medium rare state of doneness
   c. smoking, when performed slowly, maintains the natural color of meats
   d. nitrites are added to the cure

6. Which of the statements is *not* true about a panada?
   a. aids in emulsification
   b. adds significant flavor
   c. should not make up more than 20% of the forcemeat
   d. is a binder

D. Matching

Match each of the terms in List A with the appropriate letter definition in List B. Each choice in List B can only be used once.

List A	List B
_____ 1. Mousse	a. Pâté cooked in pastry dough
_____ 2. Country-style forcemeat	b. A cooked, light, airy, delicately flavored forcemeat
_____ 3. Brawn	c. A poached dumpling of mousseline forcemeat

_____ 4. Forcemeat

_____ 5. Mousseline forcemeat

_____ 6. Pâté en croûte

_____ 7. Galantine

_____ 8. Quenelle

_____ 9. Terrine

d. Meat, fish, or poultry, bound, seasoned, with or without garnishes

e. A terrine made from highly simmered gelatinous cuts of meat, wine, and flavoring

f. A puree of fully cooked meats, poultry, game, fish, shellfish, or vegetables, lightened with cream and bound with aspic

g. A whole poultry item boned, stuffed, and reshaped, poached and served cold

h. A deboned, stuffed poultry leg, poached or braised and usually served hot

i. A hearty, highly seasoned, coarse-textured forcemeat

j. A coarse forcemeat cooked in an earthenware mold

E. True or False

For each question below circle either True or False to indicate the correct answer.

1. It is possible to make a vegetable mousseline forcemeat.
   True   False

2. The best type of mold to use to make a pâté en croûte is a metal loaf pan.
   True   False

3. Sausages are forcemeat stuffed into casings.
   True   False

4. Pork bellies are usually made into bacon.
   True   False

5. Galantines are always served cold.
   True   False

6. Any type of forcemeat can be used to make a terrine.
   True   False

7. A fresh ham is made from the hog's shoulder.
   True   False

8. A mousseline forcemeat can be served hot or cold.
   True   False

9. Only hams made in rural areas can be called country hams; all others must be called country-style hams.
   True   False

10. Brining and pickling are the same procedure.
    True   False

CHAPTER 21

DEEP-FRYING

Deep-frying is a versatile cooking method that appeals to a wide variety of tastes. Following simple guidelines can ensure crisp, golden brown crusts, and moist interiors. Despite the increased health consciousness of Americans, this fat-laden cooking method has maintained its popularity.

At the end of this chapter the student should be able to:

1. Select and maintain the proper equipment and fats for deep-frying.
2. Use breadings and batters appropriately.
3. Prepare fritters and croquettes.

KEY TERMS

Recovery time   Smoke point
Basket method   Double basket method
Swimming method   Standard breading procedure
Croquettes   Batters
Fritters

TEST YOUR KNOWLEDGE

The practice sets provided below have been designed to test your comprehension of the information found in this chapter. It is recommended that you read this chapter completely before attempting these questions.

A. Terminology

Fill in the blank spaces with the correct definition.

1. Recovery time   _____

2. Swimming method   _____

3. Smoke point _____

4. Basket method _____

Fill in the blank spaces with the correct term.

5. _____ An item in which the main ingredient, diced or chopped fish, shellfish, vegetables, or fruits, are bound with a thick batter and fried.

6. _____ A mixture containing a liquid combined with a starch such as flour or cornstarch.

7. _____ Cooked meats, fish, poultry, vegetables, fish or potatoes, usually bound with a heavy béchamel or velouté sauce, breaded and deep fried.

8. _____ A standard, three-step method for breading meat, poultry, fish, shellfish, or vegetables that creates a relatively thick, crisp coating.

9. _____ A frying method used to prevent the floating of food product being cooked and therefore promote even cooking and browning.

B. Short Answer

Provide a short response that correctly answers each of the questions below.

1. What are the two main components in a fritter?

   a. _____

   b. _____

2. What is the procedure for battering foods?

   a. _____

   b. _____

3. List, in proper sequence, the five steps for the standard breading procedure.

   a. _____

   b. _____

   c. _____

   d. _____

   e. _____

4. How can one keep his/her hands from becoming coated with breading during the standard breading procedure?

_____

5. Identify the elements that damage fryer fat and explain their effects on the fat.

Element   **Effects**

   a. _____   _____

   b. _____   _____

   c. _____   _____

   d. _____   _____

   e. _____   _____

6. List two reasons why most fried foods are breaded or battered.

   a. _____

   b. _____

7. The temperature of the fat is critical during frying. List two reasons to support this statement.

   a. _____

   b. _____

8. List three ways to determine the doneness of a fried product.

   a. _____

   b. _____

   c. _____

9. List three considerations when choosing fat for frying.

   a. _____

   b. _____

   c. _____

10. Suggest three methods of holding fried products before service.

   a. _____

   b. _____

   c. _____

C. True or False

For each question below circle either True or False to indicate the correct answer.

1. The internal temperature of fried chicken should be 160–170 degrees F.
   True   False

2. The swimming method is best to use when large quantities of foods need frying.
   True   False

3. Fryolators should be purchased according to the size of the heating unit.
   True   False

4. When making fritters, the main ingredient can be raw when put into the batter, since it will cook during the frying process.
   True   False

5. Delicately flavored foods should be fried separately from foods with strong flavors.
   True   False

6. Foods that are fried together can be a variety of sizes, as long as they brown evenly.
   True   False

7. Frying is a cooking application that utilizes dry heat.
   True   False

8. Foods should be fried between the temperatures of 325 and 375 degrees F.
   True   False

9. Vegetable oils are the most common type of fat used for deep-frying.
   True   False

10. The primary purpose for beer in a batter is flavor.
    True   False

CHAPTER 22

VEGETABLES

The relatively new-found popularity of vegetables is a direct result of the demands of health-conscious patrons. Chefs have had to become responsive to such demands by using a greater variety of vegetables more frequently on the menu.

At the end of this chapter the student should be able to:

1. Identify a variety of vegetables.
2. Purchase vegetables according to needs.
3. List and explain how vegetables are preserved.
4. Prepare vegetables for cooking or service.
5. Apply various cooking methods to vegetables.

KEY TERMS

Cellulose   Concasse   Irradiation
Blanching   Parboiling   Refreshing or shocking
Beurre noisette

TEST YOUR KNOWLEDGE

The practice sets provided below have been designed to test your comprehension of the information found in this chapter. It is recommended that you read the chapter completely before attempting these questions.

A. Terminology

Fill in the blank spaces with the correct term.

1. _____   Chilling just-cooked vegetables quickly in ice water to stop the cooking process and maintain degree of doneness.

2. _____ A complex carbohydrate found in the cell wall of plants; is edible but indigestible for humans.

3. _____ Whole butter heated until it turns lightly brown and gives off a nutty aroma.

4. _____ The same as blanching, but the cooking time is longer.

Fill in the blank spaces with the correct definition.

5. Concasse _____

6. Blanching _____

7. Irradiation _____

B. Multiple Choice

For each question below, choose the one response that correctly answers the question.

1. A braised vegetable dish differs from a stew vegetable dish in that it:
   a. contains an acid product
   b. is usually prepared with only one vegetable
   c. has a longer cooking time
   d. is served with a reduction of the cooking liquid

2. Grades for all vegetables include:
   a. U.S. No. 1, U.S. No. 2, U.S. No. 3
   b. U.S. Grade A, U.S. Grade B, U.S. Grade C
   c. U.S. Extra Fancy, U.S. Fancy, U.S. Extra No. 1, U.S. No. 1
   d. U.S.D.A. Recommended, U.S.D.A. Approved

3. Vegetables are considered savory because:
   a. they are an herbaceous plant that can be partially or wholly eaten
   b. they have less sugar than fruit
   c. they have little or no woody tissue
   d. they are usually eaten cooked, not raw

4. Tofu is:
   a. used as a principal ingredient in the Chinese culture
   b. available in four different types
   c. high in nutritional value, low in cost, low in fat and sodium
   d. a fermented soybean paste stored in water with limited applications

5. The biggest disadvantage of freezing as a preservation method is that it does not maintain:
   a. flavor
   b. color
   c. nutritional value
   d. texture

6. Which of the following vegetables is *not* suitable for roasting or baking:
   a. eggplant
   b. potatoes
   c. spinach
   d. peppers

7. To preserve nutrients, color, and texture:
   a. cut vegetables into uniform shapes before cooking
   b. cook vegetables whole, then peel and cut
   c. add acid to the cooking liquid
   d. cook vegetables as little as possible

8. When steaming vegetables:
   a. overcooking is less likely to occur
   b. cover the cooking apparatus
   c. more nutrients are lost than in other techniques
   d. choose only vegetables with a firm texture

9. Which of the following is true concerning microwave cooking?
   a. It is a good substitute for all cooking techniques except broiling and grilling.
   b. It can be used as a substitute for traditional steaming.
   c. It is dangerous to use in large-scale food service operations.
   d. Its cooking process, agitating water molecules within food, depletes nutrients.

C. True or False

For each question below circle either True or False to indicate the correct answer.

1. Pureed vegetables are usually prepared by first sauteing, steaming, or boiling.
   True   False

2. Winter squash is commonly braised or stewed due to its dense texture.
   True   False

3. Food is irradiated by exposing it to gamma rays to sterilize it, slow the ripening process, or prevent sprouting.
   True   False

4. Eggplants, peppers, and tomatoes are considered "fruit-vegetables."
   True   False

5. Examples of legumes are dried beans and peas.
   True   False

6. The grading of vegetables is not required by the U.S.D.A.
   True   False

7. Potatoes, onions, shallots, and garlic are best stored between 34 and 40 degrees F.
   True   False

8. Depending on the vegetable cooked, exposure to acidity can either harm or help retain color.
   True   False

9. Flavenoids are found mainly in beets, cauliflower, and winter squash.
   True   False

10. Timing a vegetable as it cooks is the best way to determine doneness.
    True   False

D. Matching

Match each vegetable in List A with the appropriate letter in List B. Each choice in List B can only be used once.

	List A		List B
_____	1. Artichokes	a.	A winter squash variety that is popular especially in October.
_____	2. Swiss chard	b.	A type of beet only used for its greens.
_____	3. Okra	c.	Husk tomatoes with a crisp, tart flesh.
_____	4. Bok choy	d.	Tubers that grow near oak or beech tree roots.
_____	5. Pumpkin	e.	Immature flowers of a thistle plant often canned or marinated.
_____	6. Tomatillos	f.	From Arab and African cuisines, often used for thickening.
_____	7. Leeks	g.	A sweet, onion-flavored vegetable with flat, wide leaves.
_____	8. Truffles	h.	A white-stemmed variety of southern Chinese cabbage.
		i.	The immature stalks of bulb onions.

CHAPTER 23

POTATOES, GRAINS, AND PASTA

Potatoes, grains, and pastas are a great source of energy. These starchy carbohydrates are also low in fat, making them especially attractive to the health-conscious consumer. Chefs especially appreciate their versatility, variety, and ease of preparation. No menu would be complete without them.

At the end of this chapter the student should be able to:

1. Identify a variety of potatoes.
2. Apply various cooking methods to potatoes.
3. Identify a variety of grains.
4. Apply various cooking methods to grains.
5. Identify pasta products.
6. Make fresh pasta.
7. Cook fresh pasta.

KEY TERMS

New potatoes	Hulling	Extrusion
Mealy potatoes	Pearling	Macaroni
Waxy potatoes	Masa harina	Dumplings
Grains	Durum wheat	Sfoglia
Crackling	Risotto	Al dente
Grinding	Pilaf	

TEST YOUR KNOWLEDGE

The practice sets provided below have been designed to test your comprehension of the information found in this chapter. It is recommended that you read the chapter completely before attempting these questions.

A. Terminology

Fill in the blank spaces with the correct term.

1. _____ Grasses that bear edible seeds

2. _____ The most basic form of pasta; a thin, flat sheet of dough.

3. _____ The process of forcing pasta dough through perforated plates to create various shapes.

4. _____ A milling process in which all or part of the hull, bran, and germ are removed from the grain.

5. _____ Small, immature red potatoes usually marketed during early summer.

6. _____ Potatoes with a high starch content and a thick skin, also known as "bakers."

7. _____ A classic Northern Italian dish that can be made from short-grain starchy rice such as arborio, oats, or barley. When cooked, the grains should be creamy and tender, but still al dente in the center.

8. _____ The milling process in which grains are broken open.

9. _____ Raw grains are lightly sautéed, usually with onions and seasonings, and then hot liquid is added. The mixture is then covered and simmered until tender and the liquid is absorbed.

10. _____ Foods that are cooked firm to the bite.

Fill in the blank spaces with the correct definition.

11. Grinding _____

12. Masa harina _____

13. Waxy potatoes _____

14. Macaroni _____

15. Durum wheat _____

16. Hulling _____

17. Dumplings _____

B. Short Answer

Provide a short response that correctly answers each of the questions below.

1. Why is it so important to use ample water when cooking pasta?

_____

2. Why shouldn't a baked potato be cooked by wrapping in foil or microwaving?

   a. _____

   b. _____

3. Name three dishes that are traditionally made with short-grained rice.

   a. _____

   b. _____

   c. _____

4. The finest commercial pastas are made with pure semolina flour. Why?

   _____

5. Duchesse potatoes are considered the basis of many classical potato dishes. List four classical dishes using duchesse, briefly describing the ingredients.

   a. _____

   b. _____

   c. _____

   d. _____

6. Identify the three main shapes of Italian pasta.

   a. _____   c. _____

   b. _____

7. What are the three basic cooking methods for cooking grains?

   a. _____   c. _____

   b. _____

8. Give three reasons for soaking dried Asian noodles in hot water before cooking.

   a. _____

   b. _____

   c. _____

C. Multiple Choice

For each question below, choose the one response that correctly answers the question.

1. What is the difference between cooking fresh pasta and dry, factory-produced pasta?
   a. Fresh pasta takes significantly less time to cook
   b. Dried pasta should be cooked to order
   c. Dried pasta takes significantly less time to cook
   d. Fresh pasta contains different ingredients

2. Which of the following grains can be used to make risotto?
   a. Barley
   b. Oats
   c. Buckwheat
   d. Arborio rice

3. American-grown rice does not need to be rinsed before cooking because:
   a. all of the starch will be washed away
   b. the rice will become soggy before cooking
   c. rinsing will result in a sticky rice
   d. such rice is generally clean and free of insects

4. When boiling pasta, "ample water" is defined by the measurements:
   a. 1 quart of water to 1 pound of pasta
   b. 2 quarts of water to 1 pound of pasta
   c. 15:1 ratio of water to pasta
   d. 1 gallon of water to 1 pound of pasta

5. Which of the following is *not* true about converted rice? It:
   a. tastes the same as regular milled white rice.
   b. retains more nutrients than regular milled white rice.
   c. has been pearled in order to remove the surface starch.
   d. cooks more slowly than regular milled white rice.

6. Why is long-grained rice more versatile and popular than other rices? Long-grained rice:
   a. has a higher nutritional content than short- or medium-grained rice.
   b. remains firm and separate when cooked properly.
   c. is more affordable for foodservice operations.
   d. is easier and faster to cook than the other rices.

7. Which type of potato is best suited for making Potatoes Berny?
   a. Mealy potatoes
   b. Waxy potatoes
   c. New potatoes
   d. Sweet potatoes

8. Which statement is *not* true about the nutritional content of grains?
   a. They contain all of the essential amino acids.
   b. They are high in fat.
   c. They are a good source of dietary fiber.
   d. They are a good source for vitamins, and minerals.

9. Which of the following flours is used to make Asian noodles?
   a. potato
   b. bean
   c. corn
   d. oat

D. *True or False*

For each question below circle either True or False to indicate the correct answer.

1. Grains cooked by the risotto or pilaf method are first coated with hot fat.
   True   False

2. Medium-grain rice is best served fresh and piping hot.
   True   False

3. The only grain that can be eaten fresh as a vegetable is corn.
   True   False

4. Making dough with semolina flour makes it softer, more supple, and easier to work with.
   True   False

5. Asian noodle dough can be used to make dumplings.
   True   False

6. "Yam" is an industry term for sweet potato.
   True   False

7. Potatoes should be stored between 40 and 50 degrees F.
   True   False

8. The best applications for mealy potatoes are sautéing and pan-frying.
   True   False

9. A ravioli is a dumpling.
   True   False

10. For best results frozen pasta should be cooked to order.
    True   False

CHAPTER 24

Salads and Salad Dressing

Today more than ever before, salads are being revitalized on the American menu. Based on the demands of the clientele, chefs are using new and different salad ingredients.

At the end of this chapter the student should be able to:

1. Identify a variety of salad greens.
2. Prepare a variety of salad dressings.
3. Prepare a variety of salads.
4. Present salads attractively.

Key Terms

Vinaigrette	Mayonnaise	Emulsion
Tossed salad	Mesclun	Composed salad
Bound salad		

Test Your Knowledge

The practice sets provided below have been designed to test your comprehension of the information found in this chapter. It is recommended that you read the chapter completely before attempting these questions.

A. Terminology

Fill in the blank spaces with the correct definition.

1. Composed salad   _____

2. Tossed salad   _____

3. Vinaigrette   _____

Fill in the blank spaces with the correct term.

4. _____ The bringing together of two liquids that do not ordinarily form a stable mixture, with the aid of an emulsifying agent.

5. _____ A salad created by combining cooked meats, poultry, fish, shellfish, potatoes, pasta, grains, and/or legumes with a dressing and garnishes.

6. _____ A mixture of several kinds of baby lettuce.

7. _____ A cold emulsified sauce consisting of vinegar, egg yolks, oil, and flavorings.

B. Multiple Choice

For each question below, choose the one response that correctly answers the question.

1. What is the best type of oil to use when making mayonnaise?
    a. Nut oil
    b. Vegetable oil
    c. Seed oil
    d. Olive oil

2. What are the *two* forms in which lettuce grow?
    a. Bunch and leaf
    b. Leaf and head
    c. Head and stalks
    d. Stalks and bunch

3. Lettuces and salad greens should be stored in protective containers at what temperature?
    a. 30–32 degrees F.
    b. 32–34 degrees F.
    c. 34–38 degrees F.
    d. 40–50 degrees F.

4. What type of an emulsion is a basic vinaigrette?
    a. permanent
    b. semi-permanent
    c. temporary
    d. semi-temporary

5. Approximately how much oil can one egg yolk emulsify?
    a. 2 ounces
    b. 4 ounces
    c. 1 cup
    d. 7 ounces

6. The four types of salads are:
    a. tossed, green, composed, fruit
    b. fruit, vegetable, meat, dairy
    c. starch, vegetable, composed, bound
    d. green, vegetable, fruit, bound

7. In a composed salad, the green would serve as the:
   a. base
   b. body
   c. garnish
   d. dressing

8. "Tomato and Asparagus Salad with Fresh Mozzarella" would be considered a:
   a. fruit salad
   b. composed salad
   c. vegetable salad
   d. bound salad

9. Traditional potato salad is considered a:
   a. green salad
   b. composed salad
   c. vegetable salad
   d. bound salad

10. Due to the flavor characteristics of mache, what *would not* be an appropriate green to toss with this in a salad?
    a. Boston lettuce
    b. radiccchio
    c. bibb lettuce
    d. iceberg lettuce

C. Short Answer

Provide a short response that correctly answers each of the questions below.

1. What are three things that should be avoided when making a nutritionally balanced salad? The overuse of:

   a. _____

   b. _____

   c. _____

2. Give two reasons why greens should be stored seperately from tomatoes and apples.

   a. _____

   b. _____

3. List 5 of the ingredients that may be included in mayonnaise-based dressing.

   a. _____   d. _____

   b. _____   e. _____

   c. _____

4. Briefly describe the eight basic steps to be followed when making mayonnaise.

   a. _____

   b. _____

   c. _____

   d. _____

   e. _____

   f. _____

   g. _____

   h. _____

5. List the four components of composed salad:

   a. _____   c. _____

   b. _____   d. _____

6. List four possible ingredients for a fruit salad dressing.

   a. _____   c. _____

   b. _____   d. _____

CHAPTER 25

FRUITS

The versatility of fruit in cooking is astounding. Learning product identification, handling and storage techniques, and flavor combinations that enhance the characteristics of fruit are valuable references for kitchen application.

At the end of this chapter the student should be able to:

1. Identify a variety of fruits.
2. Purchase fruits appropriate for your needs.
3. Store fruits properly.
4. Explain how fruits are preserved.
5. Prepare fruits for cooking or service.
6. Apply various cooking methods to fruits.

KEY TERMS

Ripe	Nectar	Zest
Cider	Pectin	Concentrate
Papain	Jam	Ethylene gas
Jelly	Acidulation	Marmalade
Juice	Preserve	

TEST YOUR KNOWLEDGE

The practice sets provided below have been designed to test your comprehension of the information found in this chapter. It is recommended that you read the chapter completely before attempting these questions.

A. Terminology

Fill in the blank spaces with the correct term.

1. _____ A citrus jelly that also contains unpeeled slices of citrus fruit.
2. _____ The diluted, sweetened juices of peaches, apricots, guavas, black currants, and other fruits, which is often too thick or tart to drink straight.
3. _____ A fruit gel made from fruit juice and sugar.
4. _____ An enzyme found in papayas that breaks down proteins used as the primary ingredient in meat tenderizers.
5. _____ A fruit gel made from fruit pulp and sugar.
6. _____ The stage where fruit is at its full size, its pulp or flesh becomes soft and tender, its color changes, the acid content declines, and the starches convert to sugar, providing sweetness, flavor, and aroma.
7. _____ A fruit gel that contains large pieces or whole fruits.

Fill in the blank spaces with the correct definition.

8. Pectin _____

9. Cider _____

10. Zest _____

11. Ethylene gas _____

_____

12. Concentrate _____

13. Acidulation _____

14. Juice _____

B. Fill in the Blank

Fill in the blanks provided with the response that correctly answers the statement.

1. List the four fruits that emit ethylene gas.

   a. _____ c. _____

   b. _____ d. _____

2. What is an indicator of cold damage to bananas?

   _____

3. Fruits are varied in their content of vitamins and minerals. Identify the fruits that are plentiful in the elements listed below.

Vitamin C	*Vitamin A*	*Potassium*
a. _____	b. _____	c. _____
_____	_____	_____
_____	_____	_____

4. List four uses for lower grades of fruit.

a. _____   c. _____

b. _____   d. _____

5. List five methods of fruit preservation.

a. _____   d. _____

b. _____   e. _____

c. _____

6. Name four fruits that benefit from acidulation.

a. _____   c. _____

b. _____   d. _____

7. _____ is the most common method of cooking pears.
8. In classical dishes, the term *à la Normande* refers to the use of _____
9. Pumpkins, cucumbers, and melons are all members of the _____ family.
10. _____ are the single largest fruit crop in the world.
11. When deep-frying fruits, the best results are achieved by first dipping the fruit slices in _____ before submerging in the fat.
12. Name five fruits that maintain their texture when sautéed.

a. _____   d. _____

b. _____   e. _____

c. _____

C. True or False

For each question below circle either True or False to indicate the correct answer.

1. Carry over cooking occurs with fruit.
   True   False

2. The two primary methods of juicing are pressure and blending.
   True   False

3. Sulfur dioxide is added to dried fruits to maintain their flavor during storage.
   True   False

4. Freezing is the best method for preserving the fresh appearance of fruit.
   True   False

5. The highest grade of fruit is U.S. No 1.
   True   False

6. Pineapples do not ripen after picking.
   True   False

7. Irradiation maintains fruit's flavor and texture while slowing the ripening process.
   True   False

8. Papayas are also known as carambola.
   True   False

9. Tropical fruit flavors complement rich or spicy meat, fish, and poultry dishes.
   True   False

10. Fruits naturally contain varying amounts of pectin.
    True   False

CHAPTER 26

PRINCIPLES OF THE BAKESHOP

The bakeshop is one part of the kitchen that requires precise measurements and careful attention to the preparation of food product. Knowledge of the nature of the ingredients and the chemistry of baking are key responsibilities for those who work in this area.

At the end of this chapter the student should be able to:

1. Recognize and select ingredients used in a bakeshop.
2. Control the development of gluten.
3. Cook sugar correctly.
4. Explain the baking process.
5. Recognize many of the specialized tools and equipment used in the bakeshop.

KEY TERMS

Gluten	Cocoa powder	Cutting
Sucrose	Bloom	Folding
Simple syrup	Liquor	Kneading
Interferents	Liqueur	Sifting
Gelatin	Wine	Stirring
Emulsions	Brandy	Whipping
Extracts	Beating	Dough
Chocolate liquor	Blending	Batter
Cocoa butter	Starch retrogradation	Creaming

TEST YOUR KNOWLEDGE

The practice sets provided below have been designed to test your comprehension of the information found in this chapter. It is recommended that you read the chapter completely before attempting these questions.

A. Terminology

Fill in the blank spaces with the correct definition.

1. Whipping _____

2. Liquor _____

3. Simple syrup _____

4. Cocoa butter _____

5. Blending _____

6. Dough _____

7. Wine _____

8. Sucrose _____

9. Bloom _____

10. Folding _____

11. Batter _____

12. Cocoa powder _____

13. Interferents _____

14. Emulsions _____

15. Starch retrogradation _____

Fill in the blank spaces with the correct term.

16. _____ Incorporating solid fat into dry ingredients until lumps of the desired size remain.

17. _____ The tough, rubbery substance created when wheat flour is mixed with water.

18. _____ A common thickener in the bakeshop, it is a natural product derived from the animal protein collagen.

19. _____ Passing one or more dry ingredients through a wire mesh to remove lumps as well as combine and aerate ingredients.

20. _____ An alcoholic beverage made from distilling the fermented mash of grapes or other fruits.

21. _____ A strong, sweet, syrupy alcoholic beverage made by mixing or redistilling neutral spirits with fruits, flowers, herbs, spices, or other flavorings.

22. _____ Mixtures of flavoring oils and ethyl alcohol.

23. _____ Vigorously agitating foods to incorporate air or develop gluten.
24. _____ Gently mixing ingredients until blended.

25. _____ Working a dough to develop gluten.

26. _____ Also known as chocolate mass, it is the result of further roasting nibs and crushing into a thick (nonalcoholic) paste.

27. _____ Vigorously combining fat and sugar while incorporating air.

B. Matching

Match each of the terms in List A with the appropriate letter in List B. Each choice in List B can only be used once.

List A

_____ 1. Blending
_____ 2. Cutting
_____ 3. Sifting
_____ 4. Whipping
_____ 5. Folding
_____ 6. Creaming
_____ 7. Beating
_____ 8. Kneading
_____ 9. Stirring

List B

a. Use an spoon or electric mixer with paddle attachment
b. Use a whisk or electric mixer with whip attachment
c. Use a rubber spatula
d. Use a spoon, rubber spatula, whisk, or electric mixer with paddle attachment
e. Use an electric mixer with paddle attachment on medium speed
f. Use a rotary or drum sifter or mesh strainer
g. Use a whisk, spoon, or rubber spatula
h. Use a flat cake spatula or metal spatula
i. Use pastry cutters, fingers, or an electric mixer with paddle attachment
j. Use hands or an electric mixer with dough hook attachment

C. Multiple Choice

For each question below, choose the one response that correctly answers the question.

1. All fats are considered to be shortenings in baking because they tenderize the product and:
   a. leaven
   b. strengthen the gluten strands
   c. give good color
   d. shorten the gluten strands

2. Composite flours are:
   a. made from corn, soybeans, and rice
   b. categorized as non-wheat flours
   c. naturally high in protein
   d. made with the bran intact

3. Sanding sugar is primarily used for:
   a. a granulated sugar substitute
   b. making light, tender cakes
   c. decorating cookies and pastries
   d. making icings and glazes for decorating

4. The most frequently used and therefore the most important ingredient in the bakeshop is:
   a. granulated sugar
   b. wheat flour
   c. shortening
   d. yeast

5. Whole wheat flour, which includes the bran and germ, is also called:
   a. wheat germ
   b. composite flour
   c. whole flour
   d. graham flour

6. Which of the following is *not* true about the role of sugar and sweeteners in the bakeshop? They:
   a. act as a crisping agent
   b. serve as a preservative
   c. tenderize products
   d. act as a creaming agent

7. A baked good's final texture is determined by the rise, which is caused by the _____, _____, and _____ in the dough or batter.
   a. temperature, sugar, yeast
   b. protein, gluten, strands
   c. glutenin, gliadin, water
   d. carbon dioxide, air, steam

8. 160 degrees F. is the temperature at which gluten, dairy, and egg proteins _____.
   a. brown
   b. soften
   c. crystallize
   d. solidify

9. A change in a baked good's texture and starch granule structure results in:
   a. staling
   b. browning
   c. leavening
   d. gluten development

10. _____is the brown powder left after the_____is removed.
   a. Unsweetened chocolate, sugar
   b. Cocoa powder, sugar
   c. Milk chocolate, dairy solids
   d. Cocoa powder, cocoa butter

D. True or False

For each question below, circle either True or False to indicate the correct answer.

1. Self-rising flour is bread flour with salt and baking powder added to it.
   True   False

2. Glutenin and gliadin contain the gluten necessary to create a quality dough or batter.
   True   False

3. Chocolate did not exist in Europe as we know it today until Columbus brought the first cacao beans back to Spain from the New World.
   True   False

4. Unsweetened chocolate is pure hardened cocoa butter.
   True   False

5. Most white chocolate products are not made from cocoa beans since they substitute vegetable oils for cocoa butter.
   True   False

6. Chocolate will melt just below body temperature.
   True   False

7. Gluten provides structure in dough by enabling the gases from fermentation to be retained.
   True   False

8. Flour derived from the portion of the endosperm closest to the germ is coarser.
   True   False

9. Whole wheat flour has a shorter shelf life due to its fat content.
   True   False

10. Unopened bags of flour can be stored anywhere as long as the location is relatively cool and free of moisture.
    True   False

11. Beets and sugar cane are the two main sources for sugar.
    True   False

12. Unsalted butter is usually preferred to salted butter in baking because the salt may interfere with the product formula.
    True   False

13. "Carryover" cooking is a phenomenon that occurs in the bakeshop as well as the kitchen.
    True   False

14. A batter generally contains more fat, sugar, and liquid than a dough.
    True   False

CHAPTER 27

QUICK BREADS

Quick breads are popular due to their ease of preparation, versatility of application, and variety of flavor possibilities. The availability of ingredients as well as the use of chemical leaveners make quick breads an ideal option for busy foodservice operations.

At the end of this chapter the student should be able to:

1. Use chemical leavening agents.
2. Prepare a variety of quick breads using the biscuit method, muffin method, and creaming method.

KEY TERMS

Chemical leavening agents   Baking soda
Baking powder   Biscuit method
Muffin method   Creaming method
Scones   Tunneling
Streusel

TEST YOUR KNOWLEDGE

The practice sets provided below have been designed to test your comprehension of the information found in this chapter. It is recommended that you read the chapter completely before attempting these questions.

A. Terminology

Fill in the blank spaces with the correct term.

1. _____ Items such as baking soda and baking powder, which do not require fermentation, but instead release gases through chemical reactions between acids and bases contained in the formula.

2. _____ A method used to produce a tender batter with an even shape and distribution of fruits, nuts, or other ingredients. Overmixing should be avoided with this method to prevent tunneling.

3. _____ This method is very similar to the technique used for making flaky pie doughs, creating a dough that is light, flaky, and tender.

4. _____ A crumbly mixture of fat, flour, sugar, and sometimes nuts and spices; used to top baked goods.

5. _____ An alkaline compound (a base), which releases carbon dioxide gas if both an acid and moisture are present.

Fill in the blank spaces with the correct definition.

6. Tunneling _____

7. Baking powder _____

8. Creaming method _____

9. Scones _____

B. Short Answer

Provide a short response that correctly answers each of the questions below.

1. Suggest a reason why muffins might have a soapy or bitter taste.

_____

2. Why might a recipe call for both baking soda and baking powder?

_____

_____

3. What situation might call for the use of double acting baking powder?

_____

_____

4. What does the higher fat content in the creaming method do to the gluten in a mixture, and therefore for the final product?

_____

_____

5. Explain why the fat is softened in recipes using the creaming method?

_____

_____

6. Suggest a reason for elongated holes running through the center of muffins.

   _____

7. What is the basic difference between a scone and a biscuit?

   _____

   _____

C. True or False

For each question below, circle either True or False to indicate the correct answer.

1. Bread flour is used to make biscuits.
   True   False

2. The creaming method is comparable to the mixing method.
   True   False

3. Honey, molasses, fresh fruit, and buttermilk are all examples of acids that may be used with baking soda.
   True   False

4. Baking powder requires an acid ingredient in the formula in order to create the chemical reaction.
   True   False

5. Some quick breads use yeast as the leavening agent.
   True   False

6. Too much kneading toughens biscuits.
   True   False

7. Fats used in the muffin method should be in a solid form.
   True   False

8. The reason for a flat top on a loaf of banana bread is probably that the leavening agent was not sufficiently strong.
   True   False

9. When carbon dioxide is trapped within a batter or dough it expands when heated, causing the product to rise.
   True   False

10. Batters and doughs made with single-acting baking powder do not need to be baked immediately, as long as the product is refrigerated immediately.
    True   False

CHAPTER 28

Yeast Breads

Although making yeast breads may intimidate the novice baker, mastering a few basic techniques can result in a quality baked product. Beautiful breads made in-house are quickly becoming a thing of the past in the foodservice industry due to a lack of understanding of these elementary skills.

At the end of this chapter the student should be able to:

1. Select and use yeast.
2. Perform the 10 steps involved in yeast bread production.
3. Mix yeast doughs using the straight dough and sponge methods.
4. Prepare rolled-in doughs.

KEY TERMS

Yeast
Sourdough
Rolled-in dough
Wash

Fermentation
Sponge method
Kneading
Slashing

Proofing
Straight dough method
Oven spring

TEST YOUR KNOWLEDGE

The practice sets provided below have been designed to test your comprehension of the information found in this chapter. It is recommended that you read the chapter completely before attempting these questions.

A. TERMINOLOGY

Fill in the blank spaces with the correct definition.

1. Sponge method   _____

                              _____

2. Proofing

_____

_____

3. Oven spring

_____

4. Yeast

_____

5. Fermentation

_____

Fill in the blank spaces with the correct term.

6. _____ Improving the shape and appearance of some breads by cutting their tops with a sharp knife or razor just before baking; also known as docking.

7. _____ A crust is made shiny or matte, hard or soft, darker or lighter, garnished with seeds or grains, by using this glaze before or after proofing. Egg wash, water, egg and milk, and even plain flour are examples.

8. _____ A type of dough steeped in history since its "starter" was relied on by bakers to leaven the doughs prior to the commercial production of yeast.

9. _____ A procedure performed with machine or by hand, to develop the gluten which gives the dough its structure, shape, and texture.

10. _____ The simplest and most common method for yeast doughs in which all of the ingredients are simply combined and mixed.

11. _____ A dough in which the fat is incorporated through a process of rolling and folding, giving the dough a distinctive flaky texture due to the repeated layering of fat throughout the dough. During baking, moisture is released from the fat in the form of steam therefore causing the layers of dough to rise and separate.

B. Multiple Choice

For each question below, choose the one response that correctly answers the question.

1. Which is an example of a rich dough?
   a. biscuits
   b. Italian bread
   c. challah bread
   d. muffins
2. Quick-rise dry yeast uses _____ degree F. water in order to activate the fermentation process.
   a. 138 degrees F.
   b. 95 degrees F.
   c. 100–110 degrees F.
   d. 125–130 degrees F.

3. When yeast is combined with carbohydrates, the result is alcohol and:
   a. oxygen
   b. gas
   c. carbon dioxide
   d. water
4. The disadvantage of using butter in roll-in doughs is that it:
   a. has a high moisture content
   b. cracks and breaks
   c. adds too much salt to the dough
   d. needs to be clarified before using
5. Yeast products should be cooled to approximately what temperature?
   a. 32–34 degrees F
   b. 60–70 degrees F
   c. 45–50 degrees F
   d. 80–90 degrees F
6. Which of the following is *not* important when considering the amount of flour used in a yeast bread?
   a. percentage of salt in the formula
   b. flour storage conditions
   c. humidity level
   d. measuring accuracy of other ingredients
7. Commercial baking yeast was not made available in stores until:
   a. 1654
   b. 1857
   c. 1910
   d. 1868
8. There are primarily two market forms of bakers' yeast. They are:
   a. compressed and active dry
   b. brewers and compressed
   c. quick-rise dry and instant
   d. fresh and compressed
9. The primary chemical function of rounding is to:
   a. smooth the dough into round balls
   b. stretch the gluten into a smooth coating
   c. help retain the gases from fermentation
   d. proof the dough
10. When is "punching" performed?
   a. after initial fermentation
   b. after proofing
   c. during proofing
   d. after initial mixing of dough

C. Short Answer

Provide a short response that correctly answers each of the questions below.

1. Explain the two steps involved in the sponge method.

   a. _____

   b. _____

2. Why is the organism in active dry yeast considered dormant?

   _____

3. List four factors for determining the doneness of a baked yeast-leavened product.

   a. _____

   b. _____

   c. _____

   d. _____

4. List three examples of a rolled-in dough product.

   a._____ b. _____ c. _____

5. How is the quantity of dry yeast determined when it is being substituted for compressed yeast?

   _____

6. Describe the method for producing a straight method dough.

   _____

7. Briefly list the ten sequential stages of yeast bread production.

   a. _____   f. _____

   b. _____   g. _____

   c. _____   h. _____

   d. _____   i. _____

   e. _____   j. _____

D. True or False

For each question below, circle either True or False to indicate the correct answer.

1. Punching down occurs before the proofing process.
   True   False

2. Italian bread is an example of a product made using the straight dough method.
   True   False

3. Washes can be applied before or after proofing occurs.
   True   False

4. Underproofing may result in a sour taste, poor volume, and a paler color after baking.
   True   False

5. Rich doughs are baked without steam.
   True   False

6. When properly stored, compressed yeast has a shelf life of two to three weeks.
   True   False

7. Instant yeast can be substituted measure for measure for regular dry yeast.
   True   False

8. There is very little difference between the flavor of dry yeast and the flavor of compressed yeast.
   True   False

CHAPTER 29

PIES, PASTRIES AND COOKIES

The making of pastries involves a variety of techniques which, if mastered, can result in wonderful creations to grace any menu. If seen as a series of building blocks or elements, one can study classical pastries to better understand the complexities of the art which can result in the creation of a new repertoire of unique desserts.

At the end of this chapter the student should be able to:

1. Prepare a variety of pie crusts and fillings.
2. Prepare a variety of classic pastries.
3. Prepare a variety of meringues.
4. Prepare a variety of cookies.
5. Prepare a variety of dessert and pastry items, incorporating components from other chapters.

KEY TERMS

Pie	Chiffon	Éclairs
Tart	Detrempe	Paris-Brest
Pâte brisée	Bouchées	Beignets
Pâte sucrée	Vol-au-vents	Churros
Pâte à choux	Cream puffs	Crullers
Pâte feuilletée	Profiteroles	Meringue
Bake blind	Croquembouche	Cookies
Dough		

TEST YOUR KNOWLEDGE

The practice sets below have been designed to test your comprehension of the information found in this chapter. It is recommended that you read the chapter completely before attempting these questions.

A. Terminology

Fill in the blank spaces with the correct term.

1. _____ A filling that is created by adding gelatin to a stirred custard or a fruit puree.
2. _____ A paste made with flour and water during the first stage of preparing a pastry dough.
3. _____ Small puff pastry shells often used for hors d'oeuvres or appetizers.
4. _____ Larger, deeper shells, often filled with savory mixtures for a main course.
5. _____ Baked rounds of éclair paste cut in half and filled with pastry cream, whipped cream, fruit, or other filling.
6. _____ Small baked rounds of éclair paste filled with ice cream and topped with chocolate sauce
7. _____ A pyramid of small puffs, each filled with pastry cream and held together with caramelized sugar and decorated with spun sugar or marzipan flowers.
8. _____ An item composed of a sweet or savory filling in a baked crust.
9. _____ Similar to a pie except it is made in a shallow, straight-sided pan, often with fluted edges.
10. _____ A dough that produces a very flaky baked product containing little or no sugar.
11. _____ A sweet dough that is rich and non-flaky, used for sweet tart shells.

Fill in the blank spaces with the correct definition.

12. Pâte à choux _____

13. Pâte feuilletée _____

14. Bake blind _____

15. Dock _____

16. Éclairs _____

17. Paris-Brest _____

18. Beignets _____

19. Churros _____

20. Crullers _____

21. Meringue _____

22. Cookies _____

136

B. Short Answer

Provide a short response that correctly answers each of the questions below.

1. List 3 types of fillings that are used to fill prebaked pie crusts?

   a._____   c. _____

   b. _____

2. List 4 types of fillings that are appropriate for filling a crumb crust.

   a._____   c. _____

   b. _____   d._____

3. Name 2 types of fillings that are cooked by baking them *in* the crust.

   a._____   b. _____

4. List three reasons for using a flaky dough to prepare pies.

   a._____   c. _____

   b. _____

5. Why is a sweet dough, or pâte sucrée, better for making tarts?

   _____

6. When is it appropriate to use a mealy crust?

   _____

7. Why is hand mixing best when making small to moderate quantities of flaky dough?

   _____

   _____

8. What makes pâte à choux unique among doughs?

   _____

   _____

9. What determines whether a meringue is hard or soft?

   _____

10. List four uses for puff pastry.

   a._____   c. _____

   b. _____   d._____

C. Multiple Choice

For each question below, choose the one response that correctly answers the question.

1. What is the most common method for preparing cookie doughs?
   a. beating
   b. whipping
   c. blending
   d. creaming

2. Which is *not* a use for pâte a choux?
   a. profiteroles
   b. palmiers
   c. éclairs
   d. Paris-Brest

3. What do all meringues have in common?
   a. the ratio of egg whites to sugar
   b. whipped egg whites and sugar
   c. the flavoring ingredient used
   d. the method of preparation

4. Lacy pecan cookies are a cookie variety classified as:
   a. a pressed cookie
   b. an icebox cookie
   c. a wafer cookie
   d. a drop cookie

5. Egg whites will whip better if _____ before whipping:
   a. a small amount of salt is added
   b. they are well chilled
   c. a portion of the sugar is added
   d. they are at room temperature

D. *True or False*

For each question below, circle either True or False to indicate the correct answer.

1. A baked meringue containing ground nuts is a dacquoise.
   True   False

2. Cherries and apples are appropriate fruits to use for a cooked juice filling.
   True   False

3. A cream filling is basically a flavored pastry cream.
   True   False

4. Pumpkin pie is a good example of a custard filling.
   True   False

5. The ratio for making a crumb crust is one part sugar to four parts crumbs to two parts melted butter.
   True   False

6. Rice or beans can be used for blind baking.
   True   False

7. Any dough can be used to make a tart shell as long as it tastes good and has a good appearance.
   True   False

8. Italian and Swiss meringues work equally well in buttercreams.
   True   False

CHAPTER 30

CAKES AND FROSTINGS

Cake making is a science. Once the formulas and techniques are understood, the only other necessary ingredient is a vivid imagination. This chapter describes the batters, mixing methods, and presentation necessary for the perfect cake.

After studying Chapter 30 the student should be able to:

1. Describe the preparation of a variety of cakes.
2. Describe the preparation of a variety of frostings.
3. Explain some basic cake finishing and decorating techniques.

KEY TERMS

Butter cakes	Poundcakes	Glucose
Genoise	High-ratio cakes	Royal icing
Spongecakes	Icing	Ganache
Angel food cakes	Buttercream	Side masking
Chiffon cakes	Fondant	Stencils

TEST YOUR KNOWLEDGE

The practice sets provided below have been designed to test your comprehension of the information found in this chapter. It is recommended that you read the chapter completely before attempting these questions.

A. Terminology

Fill in the blank spaces with the correct term.

1. _____ An icing that is similar to flat icing, except it is much stiffer and becomes hard and brittle when dry.
2. _____ A cake that relies on creamed fat to create the structure of the cake.

3. _____ A light, smooth, fluffy mixture made of sugar, fat, and sometimes egg yolks or egg whites.

4. _____ A design cut out from paper, cardboard, or thin plastic which is used to create a design on the cake.

5. _____ Another term for a frosting that is applied as a filling and on the outside of the cake to improve the cake's appearance and shelf life.

6. _____ A cake similar to angel food cake, except for the addition of egg yolks and vegetable oil.

7. _____ A cake made by whipping egg yolks and other ingredients and then adding whipped egg whites.

8. _____ A thick sweet syrup made from cornstarch, which can be substituted by light corn syrup.

Fill in the blank spaces with the correct definitions.

9. Fondant _____

10. Ganache _____

11. Poundcakes _____

12. High-ratio cakes _____

13. Side masking _____

14. Genoise _____

15. Angel food cakes _____

B. Basic Cake Mixes Revised

Describe the **basic** steps for the preparation of the following cake mixes and give an menu example of each type of cake. Number each step in the process for revision purposes. Exact quantities are not important for this exercise.

Example: **Chiffon Cake**

1. Whip egg whites with a little sugar until stiff.
2. Add liquid ingredients, including oil, to sifted dry ingredients.
3. Fold in egg whites.
4. Bake in ungreased pan.

Menu example: Lemon chiffon cake

I. Butter cake:

_____
_____
_____
_____
_____

II. High-ratio cake:

_____
_____
_____
_____
_____

III. Genoise cake:

_____
_____
_____
_____
_____

IV. Spongecake:

_____
_____
_____
_____

V. Angel food cake:

_____
_____
_____
_____
_____

C. Matching

Match each of the classification headings in List A with the appropriate ingredients in List B. Each choice in List B can only be used once.

	List A		**List B**
_____	1. Flavoring	a.	Flour, milk, eggs
_____	2. Toughener	b.	Flour, butter, water
_____	3. Leavener	c.	Sugar, fats, yolks
_____	4. Tenderizer	d.	Flour, starches, milk solids
_____	5. Drier	e.	Baking powder, baking soda
_____	6. Moistener	f.	Cocoa, chocolate, spices, sour cream
		g.	Water, milk, juice, eggs

D. Cake Mixing Categories

Cake mixes fall into one of two categories: creamed fat or whipped egg. From the list below identify the creamed fat mixes with the letter **A** and the whipped egg mixes with the letter **B**.

A = Creamed Fat
B = Whipped Egg

_____	1. Chiffon cake		_____	6. Yellow cake
_____	2. Continental brownies		_____	7. Carrot cake
_____	3. Devil's food cake		_____	8. Gateau Benoit
_____	4. Chocolate spongecake		_____	9. Vanilla raspberry layer cake
_____	5. Sacher torte		_____	10. Sour cream coffeecake

E. Frostings Revised

Describe the **basic** steps for the preparation of the following frostings. Number each step in the process for revision purposes. Exact quantities are not important for this exercise.

I. Simple buttercream

_____

_____

_____

_____

_____

_____

II. Italian buttercream

_____

_____

_____

_____

_____

_____

III. Chocolate ganache

_____

_____

_____

_____

_____

_____

F. Fill in the Blank

Fill in the blank with the response that correctly completes the statement.

1. The amount of leavening should be _____ at higher altitudes and the eggs in the mixture should be _____. Temperatures should also be _____ by _____ F at altitudes over 3,500 feet.
2. The two cake mixing categories are a. _____, which uses _____, and b. _____, which uses _____ to create a structure for the cake.
3. Most cakes are baked at temperatures between _____ and _____.
4. Royal icing is also known as _____.
5. Pan coating consists of equal parts _____ , _____ , and _____.

G. True or False

For each question below circle True or False to indicate the correct answer.

1. The best way to cool a cake is to leave it in an area where there is a cool breeze.
   True   False

2. Frostings are not usually frozen.
   True   False

3. As a general guide for setting oven temperatures for cakes, the greater the surface area, the higher the temperature.
   True   False

4. When baking cakes pans should be filled 1/2 to 3/4 with cake mix for the best results.
   True   False

5. Angel food cake is ideal for frosting.
   True   False

6. Solid shortening is better than butter for coating pans, since it does not contain any water.
   True   False

7. Package mixes are inferior in quality to cakes that are made from scratch.
   True   False

8. The fat used in high-ratio cake mixes can be either butter or shortening.
   True   False

CHAPTER 31

CUSTARDS, CREAMS, FROZEN DESSERTS AND DESSERT SAUCES

This chapter discusses some miscellaneous items that do not fall into the general dessert categories, such as custards, dessert sauces, and ice creams, but which are essential components of the chef's repertoire.

At the end of this chapter the student should be able to:

1. Describe the preparation of a variety of custards and creams.
2. Describe the preparation of a variety of ice creams, sorbets, and frozen dessert items.
3. Describe the preparation of a variety of dessert sauces.
4. Explain how these products are used in the preparation and service of other pastry and dessert items.

KEY TERMS

Custard	Bavarian cream	Sundae
Pastry cream	Charlotte	Baked Alaska
Sabayon	Chiffon	Bombe
Temper	Mousse	Coupe
Steep	Gelato	Parfait
Soufflé	Overrun	Marquis
Crème Chantilly	Sorbet	Neapolitan

TEST YOUR KNOWLEDGE

The practice sets provided below have been designed to test your comprehension of the information found in this chapter. It is recommended that you read the chapter completely before attempting these questions.

A. Terminology

Fill in the blank spaces with the correct term.

1. _____ A gooey concoction of ice cream, sauces, toppings, and whipped cream.

2. _____ The process of slowly adding a hot liquid to eggs to raise their temperature without causing them to curdle.

3. _____ A frozen dessert made from pureed fruit, fruit juice, and sugar.

4. _____ The process of soaking food in a hot liquid in order to extract flavor into the liquid or to soften the food item.

5. _____ A dessert made with ice cream set on a layer of spongecake and encased in meringue, then baked until the meringue is warm and golden.

6. _____ A foamy, stirred custard sauce made by whisking eggs, sugar, and wine over low heat.

7. _____ The term used to describe the amount of air churned into an ice cream.

8. _____ A custard base that is lightened with whipped egg whites and then baked.

9. _____ A dessert made with two or more layers of ice cream or sherbet in a spherical mold.

10. _____ The term used to describe heavy cream which has been whipped to soft peaks, and flavored with sugar and vanilla.

Fill in the blank spaces with the correct definitions.

11. Coupe _____

12. Pastry cream _____

13. Gelato _____

14. Custard _____

15. Parfait _____

16. Mousse _____

17. Marquis _____

18. Charlotte _____

19. Neapolitan _____

20. Bavarian cream _____

21. Chiffon _____

B. Short Answer

Provide a short response that correctly answers the questions below.

1. Eggs are a high protein food and can easily be contaminated. List and describe the 6 sanitary guidelines for handling eggs.

   a. _____

   b. _____

   c. _____

   d. _____

   e. _____

   f. _____

2. Describe the basic steps and essential ingredients for the preparation of vanilla custard sauce. Number each step in the process for revision purposes.

   Ingredients_____

   _____

   _____

   _____

   _____

   _____

   _____

   _____

3. Briefly describe the 8 sequential steps in the procedure for making ice cream.

   a. _____

   b. _____

   c. _____

   d. _____

   e. _____

   f. _____

   g. _____

   h. _____

4. Describe 6 guidelines for assembling desserts.

a. _____

b. _____

c. _____

d. _____

e. _____

f. _____

C. Fill in the Blank

Fill in the blanks with the response that correctly completes the statement.

1. _____ is another name for a sabayon.
2. Pastry cream can be lightened by folding in whipped cream to produce a _____ or by adding _____ to produce a crème Chiboust.
3. Some creams such as _____ and _____ are thickened with gelatin, but others such as _____ and _____ are not, and are therefore softer and lighter.
4. When preparing a soufflé the custard base and egg whites should be at room temperature because _____ _____ and _____ _____.

D. True or False

For each question below circle True or False to indicate the correct answer.

1. Once a vanilla custard is curdled it should be discarded.
   True   False

2. A frozen soufflé is not really a soufflé in the true sense.
   True   False

3. A sherbet differs from a sorbet in that a sorbet contains milk or egg yolk for added creaminess.
   True   False

4. Still-frozen desserts have a shorter shelf life than churned products.
   True   False

5. A coulis is a fruit puree made from either fresh or individually quick frozen (IQF) fruits.
   True   False

6. Quiche is an example of a baked custard.
   True   False

CHAPTER 32

BREAKFAST AND BRUNCH

This chapter discusses the wide array of breakfast and brunch food options. The first meal of the day is the most important not only for the consumer, but also for the chef preparing this nutritious start-up for the day.

At the end of this chapter the student should be able to:

1. Describe a variety of cooking methods for eggs.
2. Describe the preparation of pancakes and other griddlecakes.
3. Identify a variety of cereals.
4. Identify a variety of breakfast meats.
5. Describe a wide variety of breakfast foods.

KEY TERMS

Shirred eggs	Pancakes
Quiche	Waffles
Omelets	Crepes
Frittatas	French toast
Basted eggs	Granola

TEST YOUR KNOWLEDGE

The practice sets provided below have been designed to test your comprehension of the information found in this chapter. It is recommended that you read the chapter completely before attempting these questions.

A. Terminology

Fill in the blank spaces with the correct term.

1. _____ This egg dish is prepared in individual ramekins lined with ingredients such as bread, ham, creamed spinach or artichokes and topped with cheese.

2. _____ A breakfast cereal made with a toasted blend of whole grains, nuts, and dried fruits.

3. _____ A breakfast dish consisting of an egg custard baked in a crust.

4. _____ Day-old bread dipped in a batter of eggs, sugar, milk or cream, and flavorings and then sautéed in butter.

5. _____ An egg dish that begins as scrambled egg and is then folded around a warm filling.

Fill in the blank spaces with the correct definitions.

6. Crepes _____

7. Frittatas _____

8. Waffles _____

9. Basted eggs _____

10. Pancakes _____

B. Short Answer

Provide a short response that correctly answers each of the questions below.

1. The egg is the most versatile breakfast item. Give 4 menu examples of egg dishes that may be prepared for breakfast or brunch.

   a. _____

   b. _____

   c. _____

   d. _____

2. List the essential ingredients and describe the 4-step procedure for making quiche Lorraine.

   Ingredients: _____

   a. _____

   b. _____

   c. _____

   d. _____

3. What is a cheese blintz and how does it differ from a crepe?

_____

_____

_____

_____

4. List the essential ingredients and describe the 8-step procedure for making shrimp and avocado omelet.

Ingredients: _____

a. _____

b. _____

c. _____

d. _____

e. _____

f. _____

g. _____

h. _____

C. True or False

For each question below circle True or False to indicate the correct answer.

1. Breakfast should provide 1/3 of the calories and nutrients for the day.
   True   False

2. Pan-fried eggs are also known as "sunny side up."
   True   False

3. The fresher the egg, the better it is for pan-frying.
   True   False

4. Boiled eggs should actually be simmered.
   True   False

5. A breakfast menu will sometimes offer steak or a pork chop.
   True   False

6. Canadian bacon should be well cooked to give a crispy finish.
   True   False

7. French toast is also known as "lost bread" in France.
   True   False

8. When preparing omelettes it is best to use uncooked vegetables.
   True   False

CHAPTER 33

Hors D'oerves and Appetizers

Hors d'oeuvres and appetizers create an ideal opportunity for the chef to showcase presentation and innovation skills. These small portions of food stimulate the appetite and tempt the taste buds.

At the end of this chapter the student should be able to:

1. Describe a variety of cold and hot hors d'oeuvres.
2. Explain the preparation of a variety of appetizers.
3. Select appetizers and hors d'oeuvres that are appropriate for the meal or event.

KEY TERMS

Hors d'oeuvre	Pressed caviar	Chafing dish
Canapés	American sturgeon caviar	Sushi
Barquettes	Golden whitefish caviar	Sashimi
Beluga	Lumpfish caviar	Brochettes
Osetra	Salmon caviar	Rumaki
Sevruga	Crudités	

TEST YOUR KNOWLEDGE

The practice sets provided below have been designed to test your comprehension of the information found in this chapter. It is recommended that you read the chapter completely before attempting these questions.

A. Terminology

Fill in the blank spaces with the correct term.

1. _____ Considered to be the best caviar, the eggs are medium-sized, golden to brown in color, and quite oily.

2. _____ The term used to describe raw or cooked shellfish rolled or served in seasoned rice.
3. _____ This is the most expensive type of caviar, coming from the largest species of sturgeon.
4. _____ A dish with a heating unit used to keep foods warm at tableside or during buffet service.
5. _____ Harvested from small sturgeon, these eggs are small and light to dark gray in color.
6. _____ Raw fish eaten without rice.

7. _____ Small skewers holding a combination of meat, poultry, game, fish, shellfish, or vegetables, baked, grilled, or broiled and often served with a dipping sauce.
8. _____ An array of raw or slightly cooked vegetables served with a dip.
9. _____ Small open-faced sandwiches constructed from a base, a spread, and one or more garnishes.

Fill in the blank spaces with the correct definition.

10. Salmon caviar _____

11. Hors d'oeuvre _____

12. Lumpfish caviar _____

13. Pressed caviar _____

14. Barquettes _____

15. American sturgeon caviar _____

16. Rumaki _____

17. Golden whitefish caviar _____

B. Multiple Choice

For each question below, choose the one response that correctly answers the question.

1. Caviar is best stored at:
   a. 34 F
   b. 30 F
   c. 35 F
   d. 32 F

2. Connoisseurs prefer to serve caviar in which of the following utensils?
   a. glass
   b. china
   c. metal
   d. plastic

3. Which of the following fish is *not* used for sushi?
   a. ahi
   b. flounder
   c. sea bass
   d. salmon
4. Which one of the following is *not* a hot appetizer?
   a. date and chorizo rumaki
   b. smoked salmon canapé
   c. chèvre tarts
   d. pouches of shrimp wrapped in filo dough

C. Fill in the Blank

Fill in the blank provided with the response that correctly completes the statement.

1. The most common canapé base is _____, but slices of firm _____ can also be used.
2. The base for canapé spreads is usually _____ or _____. They may also be bound _____ such as _____ or _____.
3. The best caviar is labeled _____, which means _____.
4. Caviar should last for _____ before being opened if stored at the proper refrigerated temperature. The best way to test for freshness is to _____ it.
5. Cold dips generally use _____ and _____ or _____ as a base. The consistency of dips can be adjusted by adding _____, _____, or _____.
6. Hot dips often use _____, _____, or _____ as a base. The traditional Italian _____ is an example of a hot oil-based dip.
7. To prevent skewers from burning _____ before assembly.
8. Wonton skins are _____ and can be stuffed with _____.

D. Short Answer

Provide a short response that correctly answers each of the questions below.

1. List the 4 guidelines for preparing hors d'oeuvres.

   a. _____

   b. _____

   c. _____

   d. _____

2. List 6 canapé spreads and an appropriate garnish for each.

   a. _____

   b. _____

   c. _____

   d. _____

   e. _____

   f. _____

3. Name and describe 4 seasonings used in sushi.

   a. _____

   b. _____

   c. _____

   d. _____

4. Briefly describe the 6 guidelines for preparing appetizers.

   a. _____

   b. _____

   c. _____

   d. _____

   e. _____

   f. _____

E. True or False

For each question below circle either True or False to indicate the correct answer.

1. An appetizer is usually served before lunch.
   True   False

2. Frozen caviar should only be used as a garnish.
   True   False

3. Most refrigerators are warmer than 32 F, therefore caviar should be stored on ice.
   True   False

4. Caviar should be served in a stainless steel bowl because it keeps it cooler than glass or plastic.
   True   False

5. Frozen fish is often used for sushi.
   True   False

6. Barquettes are ideal for a large party because they can be prepared in advance.
   True   False

CHAPTER 34

INTERNATIONAL FLAVOR PRINCIPLES

This chapter approaches international cuisine in a unique manner—that is, through the flavor principles of the country in question. Identifying these ethnic characteristics and their importance in contemporary cuisine cannot be overlooked.

At the end of this chapter the student should be able to:

1. Explain the flavor principles of several cuisines.
2. Describe chicken and starch dishes incorporating the flavor principles and representative cooking methods of each of these cuisines.

KEY TERMS

Cookery	Regional cuisine
Cuisine	Ethnic cuisine
National cuisine	Professional cooking

TEST YOUR KNOWLEDGE

The practice sets provided below have been designed to test your comprehension of the information found in this chapter. It is recommended that you read the chapter completely before attempting these questions.

A. Terminology

Fill in the blank spaces with the correct term.

1. _____ A system of cooking based upon a knowledge of ingredients and procedures.

2. _____ The art, practice, or work of cooking.

3. _____ The cuisine of a group of people having a common cultural heritage as opposed to the cuisine of a group of people bound together by geography or political factors.

Fill in the blank spaces with the correct definition.

4. Cuisine   _____

5. Regional cuisine   _____

6. National cuisine   _____

B. Short Answer

Provide a short response that correctly answers each of the questions below.

1. Describe how geographic location or climate most influences the availability of foods in the following regions of China.

   Northern China: _____

   _____

   _____

   _____

   Eastern China: _____

   _____

   _____

   _____

   Southern China: _____

   _____

   _____

   _____

2. Provide 3 examples of European/American influences on Chinese cuisine.

   a. _____

   b. _____

   c. _____

3. Japanese cuisine has traditionally relied heavily on fish and shellfish. Give 2 reasons why this is so.

   a. _____

   b. _____

4. Compare and contrast Mexican and European cuisine, listing one aspect that they have in common and one major difference.

_____

_____

_____

_____

_____

C. Matching

Match the countries/regions in List A with the dominant flavors in List B. Each choice in List B can only be used once.

List A	List B
_____ 1. Greek	a. Sour cream, dill, paprika, allspice, caraway seed
_____ 2. Eastern & Northern Europe	b. Olive oil, garlic, basil
_____ 3. Italian	c. Paprika, onion, lard
_____ 4. Spanish	d. Cinnamon, tomato, olive oil, lemon, oregano
_____ 5. Hungarian	e. Cinnamon, garlic, lard, marjoram
_____ 6. Eastern European Jewish	f. Olive oil, garlic, onion, pepper, tomato
	g. Onion, chicken fat

D. Multiple Choice

For each question below, choose the one response that correctly answers the question.

1. Which of the following countries or regions apply the quick cooking methods to meats?
   a. Western China
   b. Mexico
   c. Eastern China
   d. Northern India

2. Which of the following regions in China is distinguished by the spiciness of its dishes?
   a. Southern China
   b. Eastern China
   c. Northern China
   d. Western China

3. Rice and soy products are the staples of:
   a. India
   b. Mexico
   c. Japan
   d. Morocco
4. Sweets are popular in which of the following two countries?
   a. Morocco and China
   b. Japan and Tunisia
   c. Algeria and India
   d. Mexico and Lebanon
5. In which country would you expect to find couscous?
   a. Mexico
   b. India
   c. Algeria
   d. China

E. Fill in the Blanks

Fill in the blank spaces provided with the response that correctly completes the statement.

1. The "new cuisine" originating in France is called _____.
2. The Chinese slow-cooking method which is applied to meat is known as _____.
3. The staples of Indian cuisine are _____, _____, and _____. Lentils, peas, and beans are examples of _____.
4. Devout Muslims do not eat _____. Devout Hindus do not eat _____. Devout Buddhists do not eat _____.
5. Tabbouleh and couscous are both by-products of _____.
6. The most predominant feature of Mexican cuisine is the availability of a wide variety of _____.
7. The combination of spices that gives Indian cuisine its distinctive flavor is called _____.
8. One of the best known dishes of Northern India is _____. It is cooked in a _____ pot by _____ heat.

F. True or False

For each question below circle either True or False to indicate the correct answer.

1. The cuisine of Northern China is generally lightly spiced and uses little residual oil.
   True   False

2. Lamb and dairy products are not widely used in China.
   True   False

3. Vegetarianism is common in India for religious reasons.
   True   False

4. Curry powder is a combination of spices that is often used in Indian regional cuisine.
   True   False

5. Pork is not widely used in the cuisines of Northern Africa and the Middle East.
   True   False

6. The most common cooking methods in Mexican cuisine are sautéing and pan-frying.
   True   False

CHAPTER 35

PLATE PRESENTATION

People eat as much with their eyes as they do with their mouths. Therefore, the art of planning and executing an effective plate presentation is paramount. This is an element of planning that should be taken seriously and allowed plenty of time for planning in order to ensure success.

At the end of this chapter the student should be able to:

1. Explain the basic principles of plate presentation.
2. Use a variety of techniques to add visual appeal to plated foods.

KEY TERMS

Service	Presentation
Garnish	Composition

TEST YOUR KNOWLEDGE

The practice sets provided below have been designed to test your comprehension of the information found in this chapter. It is recommended that you read the chapter completely before attempting these questions.

A. Terminology

Fill in each blank with the correct term.

1. Service   _____

       _____

2. Garnish   _____

       _____

3. _____ The process of offering the selected foods to diners in a fashion that is visually pleasing.
4. _____ A completed plate's structure of colors, textures, shapes, and arrangements.

B. Fill in the Blank

Fill in the blanks provided with the response that correctly answers each statement.

1. _____ is a cookielike dough piped very thin and baked for use in making decorations and garnishes.
2. Proper cooking procedures can enhance the _____, _____, and _____ of many cooked foods.
3. List two ways of presenting polenta.

   a. _____

   b. _____

4. Once the color or pattern is chosen for a plate, the next important element to consider is _____, keeping in mind the amount of food being presented.
5. The _____ is often the highest point on the plate.
6. List five things that a sauce should add to a plate presentation.

   a. _____   d. _____

   b. _____   e. _____

   c. _____

7. Plate drawing is most typically done with _____ sauces.
8. List two things that a hippen masse garnish might do for a presentation.

   a. _____

   b. _____

9. List three reasons for carefully cutting foods.

   a. _____

   b. _____

   c. _____

C. True or False

For each question below, circle either True or False to indicate the correct answer.

1. A rice pilaf is a good example of a dish that molds well for an attractive presentation.
   True   False

2. The garnish should always be the focal point of the plate.
   True   False

3. Generally speaking, foods with similar textures look boring together.
   True   False

4. Dusting a plate can be done after the plating of the food is complete.
   True   False

5. A piping bag would be a good choice of equipment for performing sauce drawings.
   True   False

6. The primary consideration with sauce drawing is that the colors of the sauces used contrast with each other.
   True   False

Answers

Chapter 1

A. Terminology

1. Cooking
2. Grande cuisine
3. Fernand Point
4. Classic cuisine
5. Marie-Antoine Carême
6. Gastronomy
7. A system of staffing the kitchen so that each worker is assigned to a set of specific tasks.
8. One who shows *excessive* appreciation for fine food and drink.
9. A style of cooking that de-emphasized many classic cuisine principles and highlighted simpler, lighter cuisine.
10. A system of cooking, efficiently and economically, with knowledge and appreciation for ingredients and procedures.
11. A chef who simplified and refined *grand cuisine* and applied such changes to his work in European hotels as well as his writings which include, among others, *Le Guide Culinaire*.

B. Fill in the Blank

1. Back of the house
2. Front of the house
3. Russian service
4. Mise en place

C. Short Answer

1. a. Simultaneous cooking of many items, especially those needing constant and delicate attention

b. Cooks could more comfortably and safely approach the heat source and control its temperatures
c. Cooks could efficiently prepare and hold a multitude of smaller amounts of items requiring different cooking methods or ingredients for later use or service.
2. a. Canning
   b. Freezing
   c. Freeze-drying
   d. Vacuum-packing
3. a. Age
   b. Type of household
   c. Income
   d. Education
   e. Geography
4. a. Personal performance and behavior
   b. Good grooming practices
   c. Clean, pressed uniform

D. Defining Professionalism

1. Judgment
2. Dedication
3. Taste
4. Pride
5. Skill
6. Knowledge

E. Matching

1. a	6. d
2. j	7. b
3. e	8. f
4. c	9. h
5. g	10. l

F. True or False

1. True (p. 14)
2. False (p. 12) Today most foodservice operations utilize a simplified version of Escoffier's kitchen brigade.
3. False (pp. 9-10) Most issues in the foodservice industry that are brought to the forefront for discussion are brought about by the demands of the customer. Such concerns may eventually encourage government interaction to ensure public well-being.
4. False (p. 9) Advances in the transportation industry began to positively influence the foodservice industry during the early 1800's.
5. True (p. 5)
6. False (p. 13) Restaurants offering buffet service generally charge by the meal; if they charge by the dish they are known as cafeterias.
7. False (p. 10) A chef who prepares effective mise en place is one who is organized and ready to prepare all styles of cuisine. Proper mise en place is a habit that should be emphasized in all preparations.

8. True (p. 11)
9. True (p. 5)
10. False (p.8) Many of the preserving techniques used prior to the 19th century destroyed or distorted the appearance and flavor the foods. Therefore, when new preserving techniques were developed in the early 19th century, many of them were adopted due to their minimal effect on appearance and flavor.

CHAPTER 2

A. Terminology

1. Clean
2. Cross-contamination
3. Intoxication
4. Bacteria
5. Infection
6. pH
7. Direct contamination
8. Temperature Danger Zone
9. Sanitize
10. Viruses
11. Chemical hazard
12. A disease-causing, living microorganism.
13. A rigorous food safety system of self-inspection that focuses on the flow of food through the foodservice facility.
14. Endangering the safety of food by exposing it to disease-causing microorganisms such as bacteria, molds, yeasts, viruses, or fungi.
15. To destroy all living microorganisms.
16. A large group of plants living in the soil, air, and water, that range in type from single-celled organisms to giant mushrooms.
17. Glass chips, metal shavings, bits of wood, or other foreign matter that may cause danger to the safety of food.
18. Tiny, multicelled organisms that depend on nutrients from a living host to complete their life cycle.

B. Multiple Choice

1. d
2. d
3. c
4. d
5. c

C. True or False

1. True (p. 23)
2. False (p. 32) A licensed pest control operator should be contacted immediately. Such professionals will go beyond simply locating the source of infestation, but will also prescribe a plan of action to prevent ongoing occurrences in the future.
3. False (p. 22) Toxins cannot be smelled, seen, or tasted.
4. True (p. 29)
5. True (p. 30)

D. Food-Borne Diseases Review

1. **Botulism**
   O: Clostridium botulinum
   F: Toxin, cells, spores
   S: Cooked foods held for an extended time at warm temperature with limited oxygen, rice, potatoes, smoked fish, canned vegetables
   P: Keep internal temperature of cooked foods above 140 degrees F. or below 40 degrees F; reheat leftovers thoroughly; discard swollen cans

2. **Hepatitis A**
   O: Virus
   S: Enters food supply through shellfish harvested from polluted waters. It is also carried by humans, often without knowledge of infection.
   P: Confirm source of shellfish, good personal hygiene, avoid cross-contamination.

3. **Strep**
   O: Streptococcus
   F: Cells
   S: Infected food workers
   P: Do not allow employees to work if ill; protect foods from customers' coughs and sneezes.

4. **Perfringens or CP**
   O: Clostridium Perfringens
   F: Cells and toxin
   S: Reheated meats, sauces, stews, casseroles
   P: Keep cooked foods at an internal temperature of 140 degrees F. or higher; reheat leftovers to internal temperature of 165 degrees F. or higher

5. **Norwalk Virus**
   O: Virus
   S: Spread almost entirely by poor personal hygiene of foodservice employees. It is found in human feces, contaminated water or vegetables fertilized with manure.
   P: The virus can be destroyed by high cooking temperatures but not by sanitizing solutions or freezing.

6. **Salmonella**
   O: Salmonella
   F: Cells
   S: Poultry, eggs, milk, meats, fecal contamination
   P: Thoroughly cook all meat, poultry, fish and eggs; avoid cross-contamination with raw foods, maintain good personal hygiene.

7. **E. Coli or 0157**
   O: Escherichia coli 0157:7
   F: Cells and toxins
   S: Any food, especially raw milk, raw vegetables, raw or rare beef, humans.
   P: Thoroughly cook or reheat items

8. **Trichinosis**
   O: Parasitic worms
   S: Eating undercooked game or pork infected with trichina larvae.
   P: Cook foods to a minimum internal temperature of 137 degrees F. for 10 seconds.

9. *Anisakiasis*
   O: Parasitic roundworms
   S: The organs of fish, especially bottom feeders or those taken from contaminated waters. Raw or undercooked fish are often implicated.
   P: Fish should be thoroughly cleaned immediately after being caught so that the parasites do not have the opportunity to spread. Thoroughly cook to a minimum internal temperature of 140 degrees F.

10. *Listeriosis*
    O: Listeria Monocytogenes
    F: Cells
    S: Milk products, humans
    P: Avoid raw milk and cheese made from unpasteurized milk

11. *Staphylococcus*
    O: Staphylococcus Aureus
    F: Toxin
    S: Starchy foods, cold meats, bakery items, custards, milk products, humans with infected wounds or sores.
    P: Wash hands and utensils before use; exclude unhealthy food handlers; avoid having foods at room temperature.

CHAPTER 3

A. Terminology

1. Ingredient alternatives
2. Vitamins
3. Proteins
4. Fats
5. Minerals
6. Nutrients that must be provided by food because the body does not produce them in sufficient quantities.
7. The unit of energy measured by the amount of heat required to raise 1000 grams of water one degree Celsius.
8. All of the chemical reactions and physical processes that continually occur in living cells and organisms.
9. The replacement of one ingredient with another, presumably containing similar, but not necessarily identical taste, texture, appearance. This is done for nutritional purposes and is done for those individuals who, for dietary reasons, cannot eat a particular ingredient.
10. A group of compounds composed of oxygen, hydrogen, and carbon that supply the body with energy and can be classified as either simple or complex.

B. Short Answer

1. a. Use proper purchasing and storage techniques in order to preserve nutrients
   b. Offer a variety of foods from each tier of the food pyramid so that customers have a choice
   c. Offer entrees that emphasize plant instead of animal foods

   d. Offer dishes that are considerate of special dietary needs such as low fat or low salt

   e. Use cooking procedures that preserve rather than destroy nutrients (see p.55 for more)

 2. a. canola oil   b. olive oil   c. soybean oil

 3. a. butter   b. palm oil   c. all animal fats

 4. For a professional perspective, see page 54, "The Customers Who Count."

C. Parts of a Food Label

 a. serving size
 b. percent daily value
 c. calories per gram
 d. calories from fat
 e. recommended daily intake (RDI)
 f. daily values

D. Nutrition Review

1. c	7. g
2. b	8. k
3. m	9. a
4. f	10. e
5. i	11. d
6. j	12. l

CHAPTER 4

A. Terminology

 1. Conversion factor
 2. Par stock
 3. Table d'hôte
 4. Prime cost
 5. Metric
 6. FIFO
 7. Standardized recipe
 8. Market menu
 9. Total recipe cost
 10. A menu from which every item is priced and ordered separately.
 11. The ratio of cost of food served to the food sales dollars.
 12. The main course.
 13. A periodic check of all food items in the kitchen, storerooms, and refrigerators.
 14. A set of written instructions for preparation of the menu item.
 15. The total cost of ingredients that go into the preparation of the menu item.
 16. The cost of the item as received from the supplier, broken down into individual units.
 17. The amount of product lost during preparation.
 18. The amount of food available for consumption after trimming.

B. Units of Measure

1. 16 oz
2. 28.35 g
3. 453.6 g = .4536 k / .5 k
4. 1,000 g
5. .035 oz
6. 35 oz = 2.187 lb / 2 lb
7. 16 tbsp = 8 fl oz
8. 1 qt = 32 fl oz
9. 1/2 gal = 4 pt
10. 16 tbsp = 8 fl oz

C. Recipe Conversion

	28 portions—6 oz each	*40 portions—8 oz each*
Butter	2.5 oz	4.95 = 5 oz
Onion	10.5 oz	19.92 = 20 oz = 1 lb 4 oz
Celery	2.5 oz	4.98 = 5 oz
Broccoli	42 oz = 2 lb 10 oz	79.68 = 80 oz = 5lbs
Chicken veloute	112 fl. oz = 3 1/2 qts	212.48 = 212 fl. oz
Chicken stock	56 fl. oz = 1 3/4 qts	106.24 = 106 fl. oz
Heavy cream	21 fl. oz	39.84 = 40 fl. oz = 1 1/4 qt
Broccoli florets	7oz	13.28 = 13 oz

D. Unit Costs

To be completed in class.

E. Recipe Costs

1. $43.75
2. 85 cents
3. 12
4. $637.50
5. $6.45
6. 40

F. Yield Factor and Percentage

Total Yield Weight	Yield Factor	Percentage
8 lb	.8	80%
6.5 oz	.8	80%
27 oz	.84	84%
188 oz	.78	78%
251 oz	.63	63%
560 oz	.7	70%

G. Applying Yield Factors

A.P. Unit Cost	Yield Factor	E.P. Unit Cost
60 cents	.80	75 cents
$2.32	.80	$2.90
$1.63	.84	$1.94
43 cents	.78	55 cents
39 cents	.63	62 cents
17 cents	.70	24 cents

H. Food Cost

1. 36%
2. 83 cents
3. a. $11.61   b. $29.00
4. $1.00

CHAPTER 5

A. Terminology

1. NSF International
2. Knife
3. Thermometer
4. Oven
5. An instant source of heat for cooking, either an open flame or a cast iron solid plate.
6. A work area that is dedicated to one specific task, for example, sandwich preparation.
7. An area where several different tasks are grouped together.
8. The French chef who created "Lamb Chops Reform."

B. Equipment Identification

1. French or chef's knife—all-purpose chopping.
2. Serrated slicer—slicing cooked meat.
3. Boning knife—seperating meat from bone.
4. Paring knife—cutting curved surfaces, namely vegetables.
5. Whisk—mixing sauces.
6. Grill spatula—lifting / turning items on grill.
7. Chef's fork—carving meats.
8. Cake spatula—spreading frosting.
9. Ladle—serving soups.
10. Portion scoop—ice-cream service.
11. Stockpot—making large quantities of soup/stock
12. Sautoir—frying.
13. Wok—stir frying.
14. Sauteuse—frying.
15. Hotel pan—warming food.
16. Liquid measuring cup—measuring liquids or solids.
17. China cap—straining stocks, soups, and sauces.

18. Food mill—pureeing and straining food at the same time.
19. Drum sieve—sieving dry foods.
20. Spider—removing items from liquids.

C. Matching

1. i	6. d
2. h	7. c
3. a	8. f
4. e	9. j
5. g	10. b

D. True or False

1. False (p. 88) Stem-type thermomoters should be calibrated when dropped.
2. False (p.103) Ventilation heads should be cleaned by professionals.
3. True (p. 91)
4. True (p.102)
5. True (p. 85)
6. False (p.101) Because a steam kettle heats the kettle's sides, it heats food more quickly than a pot sitting on a stove.

E. Short Answer

1. a. Easily cleaned
   b. Nontoxic food surfaces
   c. Smooth surfaces
   d. Smooth and sealed internal surfaces
   e. Nontoxic coating surfaces
   f. Easily cleaned
2. a. Is it necessary for production?
   b. Will it do the job in the space available?
   c. Is it the most economical for the establishment?
   d. Is it easy to clean and repair?
3. a. Carbon steel
   b. Stainless steel
   c. High carbon stainless steel

F. Fill in the Blank

1. Utility	4. Buffalo chopper
2. Tang	5. Wooden
3. Griddle	6. Scimitar

CHAPTER 6

A. Terminology

1. Steel
2. Brunoise
3. Whetstone

4. Oblique
5. Chiffonade
6. Batonnet
7. Rounds / rondelles
8. A stick-shaped piece of vegetable (1/8 inch x 1/8 inch x 1 to 2 inches).
9. A small cube that can be cut from the batonnet (1/4 inch x 1/4 inch).
10. Cutting away the edges of a piece of vegetable to leave a long football shape.
11. A cube-shaped piece of vegetable measuring 3/8 inch x 3/8 inch.
12. Another term applied to finely chopped.
13. A flat cut of vegetable that is used for garnishing soups.
14. A cube-shaped cut measuring 5/8 inch x 5/8 inch.
15. A cut similar to rondelles, except it is cut at an angle.
16. A cutting technique that does not require each piece to be identical in size.

B. True or False

1. False (p. 112)
2. True (p. 121)
3. False (p. 113) A steel does not sharpen a knife. Instead, it is used to hone or straighten the blade immediately after and between sharpenings.
4. False (p. 117)
5. False (p. 113) A whetstone can be moistened with either water or mineral oil, but not both.
6. True (p. 118)
7. True (p. 112)
8. True (p. 113)

C. Cuts of Vegetables

1. 1/8 inch × 1/8 inch × 1 to 2 inches
2. 1/4 inch × 1/4 inch × 2 inches
3. 3/8 inch × 1/2 inch × 1/2 inch
4. 1/8 inch × 1/8 inch × 1/8 inch dice
5. 1/4 inch × 1/4 inch dice
6. 3/8 inch × 3/8 inch dice

Similarities: 1. Brunoise comes from julienne. 2. Small dice comes from batonnet.

D. Fill in the Blank

1. Two
   Knife tip
   Wrist
2. Tip
   Rocking
3. Away
   Steel
   Glass
   Marble
4. Heel
   Coarsest
   Finest
5. Root

CHAPTER 7

A. Terminology

1. Decoction
2. Aromatics
3. Spice blend
4. Bouquet garni
5. Condiment
6. Infusion
7. Nut
8. Oil
9. Used to add flavors, an onion piquet is prepared by peeling an onion, trimming the root end, and attaching one or two dried bay leaves to the onion using whole cloves as pins.
10. The large group of aromatic plants whose leaves, stems, or flowers are used to add flavors to other foods.
11. Strongly flavored or aromatic portions of plants used as flavorings.
12. Foods that are used in almost all stations of the kitchen with much regularity.
113. A thin, sour liquid used for thousands of years as a preservative, cooking ingredient, condiment, and cleaning solution.
14. An item that adds a new taste to a food and alters its natural flavors. The category of flavorings may include herbs, spices, vinegars, and condiments.
14. An item added to enhance the natural flavors of a food without dramatically changing its taste. Salt and pepper would be good examples of a seasoning.

B. Identification

Herb	Spice
1. Cilantro	6. Paprika
2. Oregano	7. Coriander
3. Lavender	8. Ground mustard
4. Thyme	9. Capers
5. Lemon grass	10. Black pepper

C. Fill in the Blank

1. a. Body
   b. Smell
   c. Acidity
   d. Flavor
2. Arabica
3. Robusta
4. 2 tablespoons, 6 ounces
5. a. Coffee
   b. Tea

D. Short Answer

1. a. City roast: also called American or brown roast, it can be a bit flat in flavor, and it is the roast most Americans assume they prefer because it is the roast most often used in grocery store blends.

b. Brazilian: Somewhat darker in color than city roast, it has a hint of dark-roast flavor. The name of the coffee has no relationship to its origins, and the beans should show a trace of oil.

c. Viennese: Also called medium-dark roast, this usually falls somewhere in between the city roast and French roast.

d. French roast: Also called New Orleans or dark roast, is flavored similarly to espresso, but is more smooth.

e. Espresso Roast: Also called Italian roast, is the darkest of all coffee since the beans are roasted until they are virtually burnt.

2. a. Flavorings should not hide the taste or aroma of the primary ingredients.

b. Flavorings should be combined in balance, so as not to overwhelm the palate.

c. Flavorings should not be used to disguise poor quality or poorly prepared products.

3. a. Preserves foods

b. It heightens food flavors

c. It provides the distinctive taste of saltiness

4. a. Black tea

b. Green tea

c. Oolong tea

E. True or False

1. False (p. 149) Green tea is yellow-green in color with a bitter flavor, but is not fermented at all.
2. True (p. 144)
3. True (p. 147)
4. False (p. 136) Use less dried herbs than you would fresh herbs in a recipe. The loss of moisture in the dried herbs supposedly strengthens and concentrates the flavors.
5. True (p. 136)
6. True (p. 144)
7. True (p. 149)
8. False (p.148) Café latte is made by mixing 1/3 espresso and 2/3 steamed milk without foam.
9. True (p. 146)
10. False (p. 141) A shortening is a fat, usually made from vegetable oils, that is solid at room temperature.

CHAPTER 8

A. Terminology

1. Yolk
2. Pasteurization
3. Chalazae cords
4. Homogenization
5. A non-processing technique, certification is a method of controlling the quality of milk by controlling the condition of the animals from which the milk is obtained.
6. From the French word for melted, it can refer to Swiss cheese, melted with

white wine and seasonings in a special earthenware pot over a flame, for dipping bread cubes into.
7. The clear portion of the egg often referred to as the white. It contains more than half of the protein and riboflavin and the white itself accounts for nearly 2/3 of the egg.
8. Whole butter that has had the water and milk solids removed.

B. Identification
a. shell
b. yolk
c. white
d. chalaza

C. Matching

I   1. e   6. a   II   1. e
    2. g   7. c   2. d
    3. b   8. h   3. b
    4. j   9. i   4. a
    5. f   10. d

D. Multiple Choice

1. d   5. b, c, d, f
2. a   6. d
3. b   7. b
4. c   8. d

E. True or False

1. True (p. 155)
2. False (p. 154) Shell color has no effect on the quality (grade), flavor, or nutrition.
3. True (p. 156)
4. False (p. 158) By law, all Grade A milk must be pasteurized prior to retail sale.
5. False (p. 157) The egg whites should be brought to room temperature to maximize the volume when whipping.
6. False (p. 156) Eggs should be stored at temperatures below 40 degrees F. and at a relative humidity of 70-80%.
7. True (p. 163)
8. False (p. 161) Yogurt is only as healthful, or low in fat, as the milk it is made from.
9. False (p. 162) Margarine is not a dairy product and is included in this chapter only because it is so commonly used as a substitute for butter. It is actually made from animal or vegetable fats or a combination thereof. Flavorings, colorings, emulsifiers, preservatives, and vitamins are add before it is hydrogenated.
10. False (p. 170) Processed cheese food contains less natural cheese and more moisture than regular processed cheese. Often vegetable oil and milk solids are added to make the cheese food soft and spreadable.
11. False (p. 157) Egg substitutes have a different flavor than real eggs and cannot be used in recipes where the eggs are required for thickening.
12. True

CHAPTER 9

A. Terminology

1. A moist-heat cooking method that uses convection to transfer heat from the cooking liquid to the food. Food is submerged in a liquid held at temperatures between 160 degrees F. and 180 degrees F.

2. The process of surrounding a food with dry, heated air in a closed environment. The term baking usually refers to cooking such products as fish, fruits, vegetables, starches, breads, or pastry items.

3. The proper term used for the cooking of starches, it usually occurs gradually over a temperature range of 150-212 degrees F.

4. Energy is transferred by waves of heat or light striking the food product. Two kinds of radiant heat are used in the kitchen: infrared and microwave.

5. The movement of heat from one item to another through direct contact.

6. To very briefly and partially cook a food in boiling water or hot fat.

7. A combination cooking method, stewing is most often associated with smaller cuts of food that are first cooked by browning or blanching and then finished in a liquid or a sauce. The liquid used in the second step of the cooking process completely covers the pieces of food and at a low, long simmer, the stew develops flavor, thickens, and becomes tender.

8. A dry-heat cooking method in which heat is transferred by conduction from the pan to the food, using a moderate amount of fat. Heat is also transferred to the food by the hot fat by convection.

9. This type of cooking relies on radiation generated by a special oven to penetrate the food. It is generally faster than traditional cooking methods.

10. This uses a radiant, dry-heat source located below the cooking surface and may be electric, gas, wood, or charcoal.

11. A moist-heat cooking method that uses convection to transfer heat to the food being cooked. The food must be placed in a basket or in a rack so the steam can circulate around it and cook, and the steam must also be contained by a lid-like apparatus in order to be able to cook with it.

12. Roasting
13. Sautéing
14. Coagulation
15. Convection
16. Simmering
17. Deep-fat frying
18. Boiling
19. Braising
20. Broiling
21. Induction
22. Caramelization
23. Infrared cooking

B. Cooking Methods

Cooking medium	Medium	Heat transfer method
ex: Sautéing	fat	stove
1. Stewing	fat then liquid	stove (and oven), tilt skillet
2. Deep-fat frying	fat	deep fryer
3. Broiling	air	broiler, salamander, rotisserie
4. Poaching	water or other liquid	stove, oven, steam-jacketed kettle, tilt skillet
5. Grilling	air	grill
6. Simmering	water or other liquid	stove, steam-jacketed kettle, tilt skillet
7. Baking	air	oven
8. Roasting	air	oven
9. Steaming	steam	stove, convection steamer
10. Braising	fat then liquid	stove (and oven), tilt skillet

C. Multiple Choice

1. a
2. d
3. c
4. a
5. c
6. b

D. Short Answer

1. **Braising**
   a. Large pieces of food
   b. Brown then simmer/steam
   c. Cooking liquid covers 1/3-1/2
   d. Cooking time is longer (large pieces)

   Stewing
   a. Smaller pieces of food
   b. Brown or blanch then simmer/steam
   c. Cooking liquid completely covers
   d. Cooking time is shorter (small pieces)

2. a. The food product must be placed in a basket or on a rack to allow for circulation of the steam.
   b. A lid should cover the steaming unit to trap steam and allow heat to build up.

3. a. Heat a sauté pan over high heat
   b. Add a small amount of fat and heat until just below smoking point
   c. Add dry, seasoned chicken breast (or dredge in seasoned flour), placing in a single layer and presentation side down first
   d. Adjust temperature as needed to control browning, flip when half cooked
   e. Test for proper doneness, remove from pan, and serve as requested

4. a. Bring liquid to a boil in an appropriate pan.
   b. Add food product to the cooking liquid.
   c. Adjust the temperature to a gentle simmer (160° F. to 180° F.).
   d. Test the product for desired doneness.
   e. If desired, use poaching liquid to make sauce that will be served with the final dish.
   f. Serve with appropriate sauce and accompaniments.

E. Matching

I   1. e   II 1. b
    2. c   2. d
    3. b   3. c
    4. a   4. e
    5. d   5. a
    6. g

CHAPTER 10

A. Terminology

1. Connective tissue
2. Salsa
3. Remouillage
4. Demi-glace
5. Gelatin
6. Stock
7. Jus lié
8. Venting
9. Degrease
10. Sauce
11. Mirepoix
12. Cartilage
13. Vegetables cooked in an acidic liquid used for poached fish or vegetables.
14. Proteins which are extracted from bones during the cooking process and form a jelly when cooked.
15. A sweet and sour condiment made from a mixture of fruits and/or vegetables.
16. The process of shocking food items in cold water after blanching.
17. The process by which normally unmixable combinations of food items such as oil and vinegar are forced to blend together, for example hollandaise and mayonnaise.
18. A mixture of egg yolk and heavy cream which adds richness and smoothness to sauce.
19. The process of removing caramelized particles from the bottom of a pan with a liquid.
20. A sauce made from pureed fruit or vegetables.
21. Literally means mounted with butter, swirling butter into the sauce to give it richness and sheen.
22. A combination of equal parts of butter and flour which is used to thicken sauces at the end of the cooking process.
23. A cooked mixture of equal parts fat and flour which is used to thicken sauces.
24. To cook without color, usually covered.

B. Stock Making Review

White stock; Reference: page 192
Brown stock; Reference: page 194
Fish stock; Reference: page 195

C. Sauce Review—Mother Sauces

Mother Sauce	Thickener	Liquid
1. Béchamel	White roux	Milk
2. Velouté	Blond roux	White/chicken/veal/fish stock
3. Espagnole	Brown roux	Beef stock
4. Tomato	Tomato purée	White stock
5. Hollandaise	Eggs	Butter

D. Sauce Review—Small Sauces

Ingredients Added	Mother Sauce
1. Grated cheese and cream	Béchamel
2. Shallots, tarragon, and chervil	Hollandaise
3. Shallots, white wine, butter, and parsley	Fish velouté
4. Sliced mushrooms and green / black olives	Tomato
5. Allemande sauce with mushrooms, shallots, butter, cream, lemon juice, and parsley	Veal / chicken velouté
6. Red wine, shallots, bay leaf, thyme, bone marrow	Espagnole
7. Heavy cream, crayfish butter, paprika, and crayfish meat	Béchamel
8. Mushrooms and a liaison	Fish velouté
9. Onion, paprika, and suprême sauce	Chicken velouté
10. Allemande sauce, tomato paste, and butter	Veal / chicken velouté
11. Poivrade sauce with bacon trimmings, red wine, and cayenne pepper	Espagnole
12. Sliced mushrooms, cooked ham, and tongue	Tomato

E. True or False

1. True (p. 201)
2. False (p. 202) To prevent lumps when making sauces add 1. cold stock to hot roux or 2. room-temperature roux to hot stock.
3. False (p. 203) Temperatures over 185° F. will cause the yolks to curdle.
4. True (p. 199)
5. True (p. 203)
6. True (p. 206)
7. False (p. 203) Tempering gradually raises the temperature of a cold liquid such as a liaison, by adding hot liquid.
8. True (p. 204)
9. True (p. 204)
10. False (p. 196) Fish stock should only simmer for 30 minutes.

F. Short Answer

1.
   a. Start the stock in **cold** water.
   b. **Simmer** the stock gently.

  c. **Skim** the stock frequently.

  d. **Strain** the stock carefully.

  e. **Cool** the stock quickly.

  f. **Store** the stock properly.

  g. **Degrease** the stock.

2. Hollandaise preparation: Reference p. 214

3. a. Incorrect temperature of eggs and/or butter.

  b. Butter added too quickly.

  c. Egg yolks overcooked.

  d. Too much butter added.

  e. Sauce not whipped enough.

G. Matching

1. c
2. a
3. e
4. d

CHAPTER 11

A. Terminology

1. Raft
2. Onion brûlée
3. Render
4. Bisque
5. A mixture of ground meat, egg whites, mirepoix, herbs, and spices used to clarify the stock or broth.
6. A preparation of diced, peeled, and seeded tomato.
7. A seafood soup native to the eastern U.S.
8. A soup with similar preparation to a stock except that it is more full bodied. Meat as well as bones form the basis for the soup and it is garnished with meats and vegetables.
9. A broth that is clarified to remove the impurities.

B. Consommé Preparation Review I

Reference p. 234

C. Consommé Preparation Review II

1. If the consommé is allowed to boil, or if it is stirred after the raft has been formed.
2. Stock was not degreased.
3. Poor quality stock.
4. Onion brulée omitted.

D. Cream Soup Preparation Review

Reference p. 237

E. Short Answer

1. a. Never add cold milk or cream to hot soup.
   b. Add milk or cream just before service.
   c. Do not boil soup after cream has been added.
2. Seven common categories of soup.
3. a. Beef broth and consommé both have the same base—beef stock; however, beef broth uses meat and vegetables to give it a fuller flavor and consommé uses a clarif.
      Beef broth is not served as a clear soup, but consommé must be served clear.
   b. A cream of mushroom soup uses a roux to thicken the soup, but lentil soup uses a puree of the vegetable to thicken the soup.
      They may both use stock to form the base for flavor and both may use cream to finish the soup.
      A cream of mushroom soup is usually strained before service, whereas the lentil soup is usually not.
   c. Both are cold soups, however gazpacho uses uncooked ingredients and the cold consommé uses cooked ingredients and then cools them for service.

F. True or False

1. True (p. 238)
2. True (p. 238)
3. True (p. 234)
4. False (p. 234) A consommé is a clarified broth.
5. False (p. 232) Cream soups are thickened with a roux or other starch.
6. False (p. 231) Additional items added to the soup are always referred to as garnishes, therefore the onion in french onion soup is also a garnish.
7. False (p. 242) Cold soups should be served as cold as possible.
8. False (p. 235) If the consommé is insufficiently clear, a clarification can be performed.
9. False (p. 242) Cold dulls the sense of taste, therefore more seasoning is required.
10. True (p. 245)

CHAPTER 12

A. Terminology

1. Primal cuts
2. Carve
3. Elastin
4. Marbling
5. Barding
6. Mignonette
7. Freezer burn
8. Marinating
9. IMPS/NAMP

10. Larding
11. A small round portion of meat cut from the rib.
12. A preservation method in which meat is put into a plastic container and all the air is removed.
13. To break down animals for consumption.
14. The basic cuts from each primal cut.
15. To trim or prepare an animal carcass for consumption.
16. To cut larger cuts down into portions.
17. Exterior fat or the layer of fat between the hide and the tissues.
18. Individual cuts from the subprimals.
19. A cut of meat which includes part of the rib.
20. The French for stock or base.

B. True or False

1. False (p. 265) Fresh meats should be stored at 30–35 degrees F.
2. False (p. 264) Green meats are meats that are frozen before rigor mortis has had an opportunity to dissipate.
3. True (p. 283)
4. True (p. 262) The USDA stamp only insures that the meat is processed in a sanitary way.
5. False (p. 262) USDA *prime cuts* are used for the finest establishments.
6. False (p. 263) Yield grades apply only to lamb and beef.
7. True (p. 264)
8. True (p. 264)
9. False (p. 264) Meat will hold in a vacuum package for up to six weeks under refrigeration.
10. True (p. 266)

C. Fill in the Blank

1. Good quality
2. Low   long
3. Soft   very red
   Firm   non-red
4. Dredged in flour
5. Carryover
   Retain more juices

D. Matching

1. d
2. e
3. f
4. b
5. c

E. Short Answer

Reference p. 267–286

CHAPTER 13

A. Terminology

1. Porterhouse
2. Short plate
3. Chuck
4. Steamship round
5. Round
6. Chateaubriand
7. Shank
8. The cut of meat located beneath the loin eye muscle on the other side of the backbone. It is the most tender cut of all.
9. Includes the organ meats such as heart, kidney, liver, tongue, tripe, and oxtail.
10. Located directly below the loin and can be ground or used for London broil.
11. The front portion of the beef loin, it contains a single rib, the thirteenth, and yields T-bone, porterhouse, and club steaks.
12. This primal cut consists of ribs 6 through 12 and produces full-flavored roasts and steaks.
13. Located beneath the primal chuck at the front of the carcass and is used for corned beef or pastrami.

B. Primal Cuts of Beef

1. Chuck
2. Rib
3. Short loin
4. Sirloin
5. Round
6. Flank
7. Short plate
8. Brisket and shank

C. Cuts from the Round

Subprimal/Fabricated Cut	Cooking Process/Use
1. Inside (top) round	Roast
2. Eye round	Braise
3. Outside (bottom) round	Braise
4. Knuckle or tip	Roast
5. Leg or round bone	Simmering—stocks, soups, consommé

D. Cuts of Beef and Applied Cooking Methods

Cooking Method	Subprimal/ Fabricated Cut	Primal Cut
1. Bake	Ground beef	Chuck
2. Bake	Tenderloin	Loin
3. Roast	Tenderloin	Short loin
4. Broil	T-bone steak	Short loin
5. Sauté/grill/broil	Strip loin	Short loin
6. Grill/broil	Flank steak	Flank
7. Braise	Top (inside round)	Round
8. Roast	Oven-ready rib roast/ Rib eye roll	Rib
9. Simmer	Brisket	Brisket and shank
10. Broil/grill	Skirt steak	Short plate

E. Multiple Choice

1. b
2. c
3. d
4. a

F. True or False

1. False (p. 293) The hanging tenderloin is part a part of the flank that is particularly tender.
2. False (p. 290) The chuck has a high proportion of connective tissue which makes it more flavorful than the tenderloin.
3. True (p. 293)
4. False (p. 292) Prime rib refers to the fact that the rib is made up of the majority of the primal cut from which it comes.
5. True (p. 293)
6. True (p. 293)
7. True
8. False (p. 292) Pastrami is made by curing and peppering the brisket.

G. Matching

1. c
2. e
3. a
4. b

CHAPTER 14

A. Terminology

1. Loin
2. Breast
3. Veal
4. Shoulder
5. The thymus gland of veal or lamb.
6. The breast and this portion of veal are considered one primal cut.
7. Two racks, each with seven rib bones and a portion of the backbone.
8. Meat from calves slaughtered when they are older than five months.

B. Primal Cuts of Veal

1. Shoulder
2. Rib
3. Loin
4. Leg
5. Foreshank and breast

C. Cuts of Veal and Applied Cooking Methods

Cooking Method	Subprimal/Fabricated Cut	Primal Cut
1. Braise	Hindshank	Leg
2. Pan-fry	Bottom round	Leg
3. Stew	Cubed veal	Shoulder
4. Sauté	Top round	Leg
5. Roast/sauté	Leg	Leg
6. Sauté	Veal loin	Loin
7. Sauté	Tenderloin	Loin
8. Braise	Bottom round	Leg
9. Braise	Breast	Foreshank and breast
10. Stew	Leg	Leg

D. Short Answer

1. a. Remove the shank
   b. Remove the butt tenderloin
   c. Remove the pelvic bone
   d. Remove the top round
   e. Remove the shank meat
   f. Remove the round bone and knuckle
   g. Remove the sirloin
   h. Remove the eye round
2. a. Top round
   b. Eye round
   c. Knuckle
   d. Sirloin
   e. Bottom round
   f. Butt tenderloin
3.

Primal	Subprimal/Fabricated Cut	Menu Example
Ribs:		
a.	Hotel rack	Roast veal with porcini mushrooms
b.	Rib chops	Braised veal chop with risotto
c.	Rib eye	Broiled rib eye with chipolte sauce

Any three of the following would be appropriate answers:

Primal	Subprimal/Fabricated Cut	Menu Example
Loin:		
a.	Veal loin	Roasted veal loin with wild mushrooms
b.	Loin chops	Sautéd veal chops with mushroom sauce
c.	Boneless strip loin	Roasted veal loin sauce poulette
d.	Veal tenderloin	Sautéed tenderloin with garlic and herbs
e.	Reference: page 308.	

E. Matching

1. f
2. a
3. b *d is appropriate for the breast only
4. e
5. c

F. True or False

1. True (p. 314)
2. True (p. 308)
3. False (p. 316) Sweetbreads are pressed to improve their texture.
4. False (p. 314) Émincé should be cut across the grain.
5. True (p. 311)
6. False (p. 311) The thymus glands shrink in older animals.
7. True (p. 311)
8. True (p. 311)

CHAPTER 15

A. Terminology

1. Also known as the hotel rack, this primal cut is located between the primal shoulder and loin. It contains 8 ribs and portions of the backbone and is valued for its tender rib eye muscle.
2. Mutton is the meat from sheep slaughtered over the age of one year.
3. The primal hotel rack with the breast sections connected to it.
4. Lamb
5. French

B. Primal Cuts of Lamb

1. Shoulder
2. Rack
3. Loin
4. Leg
5. Breast

C. Subprimal or Fabricated Cuts

Primal Cut	Subprimal/Fabricated Cuts	Cooking Methods
1.	a. Chops	Broil/grill
	b. Diced/ground	Stew/grill
2.	a. Chops	Grill
	b. Lamb rack	Roasted
3.	a. Chops/boneless roast	Grill/roast
	b. Medallions/noisettes	Sauté
4.	a. Lamb leg (bone-in)	Braised
	b. Boned leg	Roast
5.	a. Breast	Braise
	b. Lamb shanks	Braise

D. Cuts of Lamb and Applied Cooking Methods

Cooking Method	Subprimal/ Fabricated Cut	Primal Cut
1. Broil/grill/roast	Loin chops	Loin
2. Stew	Diced lamb	Shoulder
3. Broil/grill/roast/sauté	Lamb loin	Loin
4. Stew	Diced lamb	Shoulder
5. Broil/grill/roast/sauté	Frenched lamb rack	Hotel rack

E. Short Answer

1. Reference: Page 333
2. Reference: Page 334
3. Reference: Page 334

F. True or False

1. False (p. 330) Lamb primals are not classified into a forequarter and hindquarter as with beef, or a foresaddle and hindsaddle as with veal.
2. False (p. 330) Spring lamb is the term used to describe young lamb that has not been fed on grass or grains.
3. True (p. 330)
4. True (p. 332)
5. True (p. 332)
6. False (p. 332) The chine bone runs through the primal lamb rack.
7. True (p. 334)
8. True (p. 330)

CHAPTER 16

A. Terminology

1. Located below the loin, this primal cut produces spare ribs and the belly is cured and smoked and used for bacon.
2. The meat of pigs which are butchered before they are one year old.
3. The hind leg of the hog which may be fresh, cured, or smoked.
4. The ribs taken from the loin.
5. Spareribs
6. Picnic shoulder
7. Boston butt

B. Primal Cuts of Pork

1. Boston butt
2. Loin
3. Fresh ham
4. Belly
5. Shoulder

C. Subprimal or Fabricated Cuts

Primal Cut	Subprimal/ Fabricated Cut	Cooking Methods	Cured & Smoked	Fresh
1.	Boston butt	Broil/grill/sauté	X	X
2.	Pork back ribs	Steam—grill		X
	Pork loin chops	Broil/grill		X
	Pork tenderloin	Sauté/roast/braise/broil/grill		X
	Pork loin	Roast/braise		X
3.	Fresh ham	Roast/boil	X	X
4.	Spare ribs	Simmer—grill	X	X
	Bacon	Sauté/grill	X	
5.	Picnic shoulder	Bake	X	X

D. Cuts of Pork and Applied Cooking Methods

Reference: Page 357–365

E. Short Answer

1. Reference: Page 354
2. a. Shoulder
   b. Shoulder hock
   c. Boston butt—cottage ham
   d. Spare ribs—belly
   e. Pork belly—bacon
   f. Boneless pork loin—Canadian bacon
   g. Fresh ham

F. Matching

1. d
2. f
3. a
4. b
5. c

G. True or False

1. False (p. 350) The Boston butt is located in the forequarter.
2. True (p. 350)
3. True (p. 353)
4. False (p. 350) The foreshank is called the shoulder hock.
5. False (p. 352) Center-cut pork chops are the choicest chops from the primal loin.
6. False (p. 353) Canadian is made from the boneless pork loin.
7. True (p. 353)
8. True (p. 352)
9. False (p. 350)
10. False (p. 350)

CHAPTER 17

A. Terminology

1. A collective name given to livers, gizzards, hearts, and necks.
2. Trussing is tying the bird into a more compact shape using butcher's twine.
3. A surgically castrated male chicken.
4. A chicken suprême or airline breast is half of a boneless chicken breast with the first wing bone attached.
5. A point
6. Game hen
7. Foie gras

B. Short Answer

1. Reference: Page 385
2. Similarity: Overused muscles are more tough than underused ones.
   Difference: Red meat has marbling—poultry does not.
3. Reference: Page 374
4. Reference: Page 365
5. Chicken, duck, goose, guinea, pigeon, and turkey.
7. a. Be sure all work surfaces and equipment are clean.
   b. Avoid getting poultry juices in contact with other food.
   c. Anything coming in contact with raw poultry should be sanitized before it comes in contact with any other food.
   d. Cooked foods should never be placed in containers that were used to hold the raw product.
   e. Kitchen towels used to handle poultry should be sanitized before being reused to prevent cross-contamination.
8. Reference: Page 376

C. Matching

1. b
2. e
3. a
4. f
5. c

D. Fill in the Blank

1. Protein
   Myoglobin
2. 165 and 170°F
3. Roaster duckling
   Dark
   Fat
4. White wine or lemon, oil, salt, pepper, herbs and spices.
   Barbecue sauce

E. Multiple Choice

1. c
2. b
3. a

F. True or False

1. False (p. 368) Poultry fat has a lower melting point than other animal fats.
2. True (p. 384)
3. True (p. 369)
4. False (p. 380) Poultry that is left too long in an acidic marinade may take on undesirable flavors.
5. False (p. 369) The cooking time for dark meat is longer.
6. False (p. 374) Poultry should be frozen at −18° C/0° F or below.
7. False (p. 369) The skin color of poultry is related to what it is fed.
8. True (p. 373)
9. False (p. 369) Older male birds have less flavor than older female birds.
10. False (p. 372) Overcooking foie gras will cause it to melt away.
11. False (p. 371) A young pigeon is known as a squab.
12. False (p. 372) The gizzard is the bird's stomach.

CHAPTER 18

A. Terminology

1. Game
2. Hanging
3. The term used to describe deer meat.
4. Another word for bison—animals which used to roam the plains states and almost became extinct.

B. Short Answer

1. a. sausages
   b. forcemeats
   c. pâtés
2. Reference: Page 422
3. Reference: Page 417
4. Reference: Page 422

C. Multiple Choice

1. b
2. c
3. b
4. a
5. d
6. c

D. True or False

1. True (p. 421)
2. True (p. 421)
3. False (p. 419) Mature boar is one or two years old.
4. False (p. 422) Wild game can only be served by those who hunt and share their kill.
5. True (p. 419)
6. False (p. 421) Game is lower in fat and higher in protein and minerals than other meats.
7. False (p. 417) There is no marbling in venison flesh.
8. False (p. 416) Large game animals are available only precut into subprimals or portions.
9. True (p. 416)
10. True (p. 416)

CHAPTER 19

A. Terminology

1. En papillote
2. Mollusks
3. Aquafarming
4. Pan-dressed
5. Round fish
6. Crustaceans
7. Steak
8. Drawn
9. The side of a fish is removed intact boneless or semi-boneless, with or without the skin.
10. A slice cut, usually on an angle from fillets of large flat or round fish.
11. The viscera, gills, fins, and scales are removed from the fish.
12. These fish have asymmetrical, compressed bodies, swim in a horizontal position and are found in deep ocean waters around the world. Both eyes are on one side of the head, their scales are small, and their dorsal and anal fins run the length of their bodies.
13. Used for swordfish and sharks, which are cut into large boneless pieces from which steaks are then cut.

B. Multiple Choice

1. b		7. a	
2. d		8. d	
3. c		9. c	
4. a		10. d	
5. d		11. c	
6. b		12. c	

C. Market Forms of Fish

1. drawn
2. pan-dressed
3. fillets
4. whole or round
5. steaks
6. butterflied fillets
7. wheel or center cut

D. Short Answer

1. a. they cook evenly
   b. they cook quickly
2. a. translucent flesh becomes opaque
   b. flesh becomes firm
   c. flesh separates from the bones easily
   d. flesh begins to flake
3. a. shallow poach
   b. sauté
   c. broil
   d. bake
4. oily
   a. trout
   b. swordfish
   lean
   c. bass
   d. snapper
5. a. scallops
   b. lobster
   c. shrimp
   d. crab
6. a. baked stuffed shrimp
   b. oysters Rockefeller
   c. baked stuffed lobster
7. a. they are naturally tender
   b. they cook relatively quickly
8. a. eyes
   b. gills
   c. fins and scales
   d. smell

E. True or False

1. False (p. 453) Only fish processed under Type 1 inspection services are eligible for grading.
2. False (p. 452) Fish and shellfish inspections are voluntary and are performed in a fee-for-service program.
3. True (p. 450)
4. True (p. 467)
5. False (p. 451) Maine lobsters have meat both in their tails and claws and are considered superior in flavor to all other lobsters. Spiny lobsters primarily have meat in the tails.
6. False (p. 447) Atlantic hard-shell clams are also known as quahogs.

7. True (p. 471)
8. False (p. 473) En papillote is actually an example of steaming.
9. False (p. 452) In general, shellfish has less cholesterol than lamb and other meats.
10. False (p. 476) A cuisson is the liquid used when shallow poaching.

CHAPTER 20

A. Terminology

1. Smoking
2. Brine
3. Sausage
4. Basic forcemeat
5. Rillettes
6. Terrine
7. Confit
8. Quenelles
9. Brawns
10. A traditional country-style forcemeat is heavily seasoned with onions, garlic, pepper, juniper berries, and bay leaves. It is the simplest of the forcemeats to prepare.
11. A mixture of salt and sodium nitrite.
12. Made from forcemeats of poultry, game, or suckling pig and wrapped in the skin of the bird or animal and poached in an appropriate stock.
13. Pâtés baked in pastry.
14. A savory jelly produced by increasing the gelatin content of a strong stock and then clarifying the stock like a consommé.
15. Traditionally a fine savory meat filling wrapped in pastry, baked, and served hot or cold.
16. A light, airy, and delicately flavored forcemeat. It is usually made with fish or shellfish, but also pork, veal, feathered game, or poultry. Often egg whites and cream are added to lighten the texture.
17. Similar to a galantine, it is made by removing the bones of a poultry leg, filling the cavity with an appropriate forcemeat, and poaching or braising the leg with vegetables, serving it hot.
18. Something other than fat that is added to a forcemeat to enhance smoothness, and aid in emulsification.

B. Short Answer

1. a. basic forcemeat
   b. country-style forcemeat
   c. mousseline forcemeat
2. Add small quantities of crushed ice, bit by bit, to the machine while it is grinding.

3.	*galantine*	*ballottine*
	a. uses whole chickens, ducks, etc.	uses poultry legs
	b. all bones are removed	all bones are removed
	c. cavity of bird is filled with forcemeat	cavity of leg is filled with forcemeat
	d. it is wrapped in skin, plastic, cheescloth	cooked without wrapping
	e. it is poached	it is poached or braised
	f. always served cold	usually served hot

4. a. keep a precise ratio of fat to other ingredients
   b. maintain temperatures below 40 degrees F. during preparation
   c. mix ingredients properly
5. a. to glaze, preventing drying out and oxidation of food
   b. to cut into decorative garnish
   c. to add flavor and shine
   d. to bind mousses and salads
   e. to fill cooked pâtés én croûte

C. Multiple Choice

1. a	4. a
2. c	5. d
3. c	6. b

D. Matching

1. f	6. a
2. i	7. g
3. e	8. c
4. d	9. j
5. b	

E. True or False

1. False (p. 517) Mousseline forcemeats can only be made out of meats, poultry, fish, or shellfish.
2. False (p. 520) The best type of mold to use is a collapsible, hinged, thin metal pan.
3. True (p. 528)
4. True (p. 530)
5. True (p. 526)
6. True (p. 521)
7. False (p. 531) A fresh ham is made from the pig's hind leg.
8. True (p. 517)
9. True (p. 531)
10. True (p. 529)

CHAPTER 21

A. Terminology

1. The length of time it takes the fat to return to the desired cooking temperature after food is submerged in it.
2. The preferred method for frying battered foods which would otherwise sink to the bottom of food baskets and stick during the cooking process.
3. The temperature at which the fat/oil visibly begins to smoke and chemically begins to break down.
4. A deep-frying method that uses a basket to hold foods that don't tend to stick together.
5. Fritters
6. Batters
7. Croquettes
8. Standard breading procedure
9. Double basket method

B. Short Answer

1. a. Diced nutritional ingredient
   b. Thick batter
2. a. Pat food dry and dredge in flour (if desired).
   b. Dip item in batter and place directly in hot fat without the use of food baskets.
3. a. Product to be breaded
   b. Flour
   c. Egg wash
   d. Bread crumbs
   e. Pan to hold final product
4. Use one hand for dipping the food into the liquid ingredients and one hand to dip into the dry ingredients.
5.

Element	Effects
a. Salt	fat becomes dark
b. Water	fat smokes
c. Overheating	fat foams
d. Food particles	fat develops flavors
e. Oxygen	fat becomes rancid

6. a. Helps to keep food moist
   b. Prevents excessive greasiness
7. a. The fat must be hot enough to quickly seal the surface of the food so it doesn't become excessively greasy.
   b. The fat shouldn't be so hot that the food's surface burns before the interior is cooked.
8. a. The color of the final product is an even, golden brown *providing that* the food is also cooked on the interior.
   b. Large items like fried chicken can be tested with a thermometer.
   c. The exterior of the fried product, including potatoes, should be crisp.
9. a. Flavor
   b. Smoke point
   c. Resistance to chemical breakdown

10. Fried foods
    a. should be kept under a heat lamp
    b. should be placed in a pan lined with absorbent paper on a rack.
    c. should not be stored in steam tables.

C. True or False

1. True (p. 560)
2. False (p. 553) This method is best used for foods that float, therefore the second basket is placed on top of the food to ensure total submersion in the hot fat.
3. False (p. 550) Fryolators are sized by the amount of fat they hold.
4. False (p. 558) It is preferred to cook and cool the main ingredient before mixing it with batter. Otherwise, since the frying time is relatively short in most instances, it is likely that the uncooked ingredient would not cook in time.
5. True (p. 553)
6. False (p. 553) Foods that are fried together should be the same size and thickness so they cook evenly.
7. True (p. 500)
8. True (p. 552)
9. True (p. 551)
10. False (p. 556) The primary purpose is leavening, flavor is an added benefit.

CHAPTER 22

A. Terminology

1. Refreshing or shocking
2. Cellulose
3. Beurre noisette
4. Parboiling
5. Peeled, seeded, and diced tomatoes
6. Briefly or partially cooking a food in boiling water or hot fat
7. Exposing food to gamma rays in order to sterilize, prevent sprouting, and slow ripening.

B. Multiple Choice

1. b
2. c
3. b
4. c
5. d
6. c
7. d
8. b
9. b

C. True or False

1. False (p. 603) Pureed vegetables are usually prepared by baking, boiling, steaming, or microwaving.
2. False (p. 601) Green leafy vegetables and winter squash are generally not braised or stewed.

3. True (p. 588)
4. True (p. 567)
5. True (p. 579)
6. True (p. 587)
7. False (p. 588) They are usually stored at 40-60 degrees F.
8. True (p. 590)
9. False (p. 591) Red and white vegetables such as red cabbage, beets, and cauliflower contain flavenoids.
10. False (p. 591) Testing the texture, looking for an al dente consistency, is generally the best determination of doneness.

D. Matching

1. e
2. b
3. f
4. h

5. a
6. c
7. g
8. d

CHAPTER 23

A. Terminology

1. Grains
2. Sfoglia
3. Extrusion
4. Pearling
5. New potatoes
6. Mealy potatoes
7. Risotto
8. Cracking
9. Pilaf
10. Al dente
11. A milling process in which grains are reduced to a powder.
12. A finely ground flour made from hominy used for making breads, tortillas, tomales, etc.
13. Those varieties that have a low starch content and thin skin.
14. Any dried pasta made with wheat flour and water
15. A hard wheat milled into semolina and used for making pasta.
16. A milling process in which the hull is removed from the grains.
17. A small mound of dough cooked by steaming or simmering in a flavorful liquid.

B. Short Answer

1. To allow the pasta ample space to move freely and so that the starches that are released don't cause the pasta to become gummy and sticky.
2. a. Wrapping the potato in foil causes it to steam instead of bake and the skin will be soggy.
   b. Microwaving also causes steaming to occur and causes the skin to be soggy.

3. a. Italian risotto
   b. Spanish paella
   c. Japanese sushi
4. This gives the dough a rich, yellow color, and the dough is more resilient to the machinery during high-scale production. It also produces pasta that has a lightly pitted surface, causing the pasta to absorb sauces well.
5. a. Duchesse + tomato concasse=Marquis
   b. Duchesse + chopped truffles, almond coating, and deep-fried=Berny
   c. Duchesse + pâte à choux=Dauphine
   d. Dauphine + grated parmesan, piped, and deep-fried=Lorette
6. a. Ribbon
   b. Tubes
   c. Shapes
7. a. Simmering
   b. Pilaf
   c. Risotto
8. a. The water softens the noodle strands.
   b. The bundles begin to separate.
   c. The noodles cook more evenly.

C. Multiple Choice

1. a
2. c
3. d
4. d
5. c
6. b
7. b
8. b
9. b

D. True or False

1. True (p. 631)
2. True (p. 627)
3. True (p. 626)
4. False (p. 639) Semolina flour, although it makes the dough more yellow, makes a dough tougher and more difficult to work with.
5. True (p. 641)
6. False (p. 619) A yam is botanically different from both sweet and common potatoes. Although it is less sweet than a sweet potato, it can be used interchangeably.
7. False (p. 620) Potatoes should be stored between 50 and 60 degrees F.
8. False (p. 623) Waxy potatoes are best for these applications.
9. True (p. 638)
10. True (p. 641)

CHAPTER 24

A. Terminology

1. A more elegant version of the green salad that uses the green as the base and artistically arranges the other ingredients on top. It usually has four components.

2. An informal green salad that tosses all ingredients; greens, dressing, and garnish, in a bowl before plating.
3. A temporary emulsion of oil, and vinegar with the addition of seasonings.
4. Emulsion
5. Bound salad
6. Mesclun
7. Mayonnaise

B. Multiple Choice

1. b   6. d
2. b   7. a
3. c   8. c
4. c   9. d
5. d   10. b

C. Short Answer

1. a. Cheese and other high-fat dairy products
   b. Most meats (especially if high in fat)
   c. Most emulsified dressings
2. a. The gas causes the greens to wilt.
   b. Accelerates spoilage
3. a. Buttermilk   d. Spices
   b. Vinegar   e. Vegetables
   c. Herbs
4. a. Bring mise en place up to room temperature.
   b. In the bowl of an electric mixer, whip the egg yolks until frothy.
   c. Add seasonings to the yolks and combine.
   d. Add a small amount of liquid from the recipe and combine.
   e. Begin whipping on high speed and slowly drizzle in oil until emulsion starts.
   f. After the emulsion forms, slow the mixer and add the oil a bit faster.
   g. When the mayonnaise is thick, add a small amount of the liquid from the recipe. Alternate this process with the oil until all incorporated.
   h. Taste, adjust seasonings, and refrigerate immediately.
5. a. base   c. garnish
   b. body   d. dressing
6. a. liqueur   c. yogurt
   b. fruit puree   d. sweetener, such as honey

CHAPTER 25

A. Terminology

1. Marmalade
2. Nectar
3. Jelly
4. Papain
5. Jam

6. Ripe
7. Preserve
8. A carbohydrate obtained from certain fruits; used to thicken jams and jellies.
9. Mildly fermented apple juice.
10. The thin, colored part of a citrus peel.
11. A colorless, odorless hydrocarbon gas naturally emitted from fruits and fruit-vegetables that encourages ripening,
12. Also known as a fruit paste or compound, is a reduced fruit puree used as a flavoring.
13. Immersing cut fruits in an acidic solution to retard enzymatic browning.
14. The liquid extracted from any fruit or vegetable.

B. Fill in the Blank

1. a. bananas   c. apples
   b. tomatoes   d. melons
2. A grayish cast or color on the fruit
3. a. citrus, melons, and strawberries
   b. apricots, mangos, and kiwis
   c. bananas, raisins, and figs
4. Process the fruit into:
   a. sauces   c. jellies
   b. jams   d. preserves
5. a. irradiation   d. acidulation
   b. canning   e. drying
   c. freezing
6. a. apples   c. pears
   b. bananas   d. peaches
7. poaching
8. apples
9. gourd
10. grapes
11. batter
12. a. apples   d. bananas
    b. cherries   e. pineapples
    c. pears

C. True or False

1. True (p. 721)
2. True (p. 720)
3. False (p. 720) Sulfur dioxide is added to prevent browning and extend the shelf life.
4. False (p. 719) Freezing is generally one of the worst preserving methods for preserving the natural appearance since all fruits are 75-95% water which seeps out of the fruit when it defrosts.
5. False (p. 717) The highest grade is U.S. Fancy.
6. True (p. 716)
7. True (p. 719)
8. False (p. 714) Papayas are also referred to as paw paws.
9. True (p. 712)
10. True (p. 726)

CHAPTER 26

A. TERMINOLOGY

1. Beating vigorously to incorporate air
2. An alcoholic beverage made by distilling grains, vegetables, or other foods, may include rum, whiskey, and vodka.
3. Sugar that is liquefied by combining it with water so it then can be incorporated into certain prepared items in this liquid form.
4. The fat found in chocolate mass which usually averages about 53%.
5. Mixing two or more ingredients until evenly distributed.
6. One form of a baked good that has a low water content compared to a batter. The other ingredients are embedded in gluten that is developed by beating, blending, cutting, or kneading.
7. An alcoholic beverage made from the fermented juice of grapes.
8. The most common form of refined sugar in the kitchen that is obtained from sugar cane or beets.
9. The migration of cocoa butter crystals to the surface of chocolate during storage due to temperature change. Bloom appears in the form of grayish-white spots, will disappear when chocolate is melted, and does not affect the flavor or function of chocolate.
10. Very gently incorporating ingredients, such as dry ingredients with whipped eggs.
11. A mixture containing more fat, sugar, and liquids than a dough, with minimum gluten development. It is usually prepared by blending, creaming, stirring, or whipping and is thin enough to pour.
12. The brown powder resulting from removing virtually all of the cocoa butter from the chocolate liquor.
13. Ingredients, such as cream of tartar, vinegar, and glucose, that interfere with the formation of sugar crystals.
14. Flavoring oils mixed into water with the aid of emulsifiers.
15. Also known as staling, it is a general loss in the moisture of a baked good which includes a change in the location and distribution of water molecules within the product.
16. Cutting
17. Gluten
18. Gelatin
19. Sifting
20. Brandy
21. Liqueur
22. Extracts
23. Beating
24. Stirring
25. Kneading
26. Chocolate liquor
27. Creaming

B. Matching

1. d
2. i

6. e
7. a

3. f	8. j
4. b	9. g
5. c	

C. Multiple Choice

1. d	6. a
2. b	7. d
3. c	8. d
4. b	9. a
5. d	10. d

D. True or False

1. False (p. 742) Self-rising flour is all-purpose flour with salt and baking powder added to it.
2. False (p. 741) Glutenin and gliadin are the proteins which, when introduced to moisture and manipulated, form gluten.
3. True (p. 753)
4. False (p. 754) Unsweetened chocolate is 100% chocolate liquor.
5. True (p. 755)
6. True (p. 754)
7. True (p. 741)
8. False (p. 741) Flour derived from this portion of the endosperm is finer than other flours.
9. True (p. 742)
10. False (p. 745) Unopened flour should be stored in the manner described, except it is also very important to store it away from strong odors, as it will absorb them easily.
11. True (p. 743)
12. True (p. 750) In addition to these qualities, unsalted butter tends to be preferred because it is generally fresher than salted butter.
13. True (p. 759)
14. True (p. 757)

CHAPTER 27

A. Terminology

1. Chemical leavening agents
2. Muffin method
3. Biscuit method
4. Streusel
5. Baking soda
6. Overmixing causes toughness and may cause holes to form inside the baked product.
7. Sodium bicarbonate and one or more acids, generally cream of tartar and/or sodium aluminum sulfate. It also contains a starch to prevent lumping and balance chemical reactions.

8. Much like the mixing method, it produces products with a fine, cakelike texture. It usually contains a higher fat content which tenderized the batter and lessens the danger of overmixing.
9. Made with the biscuit method, this biscuit of English origin usually contains eggs and butter.

B. Short Answer

1. The bitter or soapy flavor, and sometimes yellow coloring, is often caused by too much baking soda that may not have been properly mixed into the batter.
2. Baking soda can only release carbon dioxide to the extent that there is also an acid present in the formula. If the soda/acid reaction alone is insufficient to leaven the product, baking powder is needed for additional leavening.
3. Batters/doughs that may sit for some time before baking often use double-acting baking powder, which has a second leavening action that is activated only with the application of heat.
4. The higher fat content in the creaming method shortens the strands of gluten and therefore makes the final product more tender.
5. Softening the fat makes it easier to cream it with the sugar and therefore creates better aeration.
6. Overmixing the batter.
7. A scone is seen by many as a rich biscuit that also has butter and eggs in it. It is speculated that biscuits, at least the American form of the word, contain a less expensive type of fat, such as lard, and will omit the eggs.

C. True or False

1. False (p.766) All-purpose flour is used in all biscuit methods.
2. True (p. 769)
3. True (p. 764)
4. False (p. 764) Baking powder already contains both an acid and a base and therefore only moisture is needed to induce the release of gases.
5. False (p. 764) All quick breads use chemical leavening agents; because they don't need to ferment like yeast-leavened doughs, they are considered "quick."
6. True (p. 766)
7. False (p. 769) Fats used in the muffin method should be in the liquid form.
8. False (p. 771) The leavening agent was there, so the assumption should be that the oven temperature was too low.
9. True (p. 764)
10. False (p. 765) Batters and doughs made with single-acting baking powder should be baked as soon as they are assembled and mixed together.

CHAPTER 28

A. Terminology

1. A method of mixing yeast doughs in two stages. In the first stage, the yeast, liquid, and approximately one half of the flour are combined to make a thick batter known as the sponge which is allowed to rise until bubbly and double in size. The second stage involves mixing in the rest of the flour as well as

the salt, fat, and sugar. The dough is kneaded and allowed to rise again.
2. The rise given to shaped yeast products just prior to baking.
3. It is what occurs when yeast products are first put in the oven, the gases expand, and the product experiences a sudden rise.
4. A living organism, it is a one-celled fungus.
5. This organic process occurs when yeast feeds on carbohydrates, converting the sugars into carbon dioxide and alcohol.
6. Slashing
7. Wash
8. Sourdough
9. Kneading
10. Straight dough method
11. Rolled-in dough

B. Multiple Choice

1. c	6. a
2. d	7. d
3. c	8. a
4. b	9. c
5. b	10. a

C. Short Answer

1. a. The yeast, liquid, and approximately one half of the flour are combined to make a thick batter known as a sponge, which is allowed to rise until bubbly and doubled in size.
   b. Then the salt, fat, sugar, and remaining flour are added. The dough is then kneaded and allowed to rise again. This creates a different flavor and a lighter texture than breads made with the straight dough method.
2. The organism is considered dormant because virtually all of the moisture has been removed, which helps to increase the shelf life, among other things.
3. a. product size
   b. the thermostat's accuracy
   c. crust color
   d. tapping loaf on the bottom and listening for hollow sound
4. a. croissants
   b. danish pastries
   c. non-yeast-leavened pastry
5. Halve the specified weight of compressed yeast when substituting dry yeast in a formula.
6. Combine all ingredients and mix.
7. a. Scale ingredients
   b. Mix and knead dough
   c. Ferment dough
   d. Punch down dough
   e. Portion dough
   f. Round portions
   g. Shape portions
   h. Proof products
   i. Bake products
   j. Cool and store finished products

D. True or False

1. True (p. 785) More specifically, though, it occurs just after fermentation.
2. True (p. 784)
3. True (p. 789)
4. False (p. 788) Underproofing results in poor volume and texture.
5. True (p. 789)
6. True (p. 781)
7. True (p. 781)
8. True (p. 781)

CHAPTER 29

A. Terminology

1. Chiffon
2. Detrempe
3. Bouchees
4. Vol-au-vents
5. Cream puffs
6. Profiteroles
7. Croquembouche
8. Pie
9. Tart
10. Pâte brisée
11. Pâte sucrée
12. A dough cooked before baking, it has batterlike smoothness with a firm texture.
13. Another term for puff pastry, it is a rich, buttery dough that bakes into hundreds of light, crispy layers.
14. To bake a pie shell before it is filled, lining it with parchment paper and rice or beans during baking.
15. Pricking small holes in an unbaked dough or crust to allow steam to escape and to prevent the dough from rising when baked.
16. Baked fingers of pâte à choux filled with pastry cream; the top is then coated with chocolate glaze or fondant.
17. Rings of baked pâte à choux cut in half horizontally and filled with pastry cream and/or flavored whipped cream. The top is dusted with powdered sugar or drizzled with chocolate glaze.
18. Squares or strips of pâte à choux deep-fried and dusted with powdered sugar.
19. A Spanish and Mexican pastry in which sticks of pâte à choux flavored with cinnamon are deep-fried and rolled in sugar while still hot.
20. A Dutch pastry in which a loop or strip of twisted pâte à choux is deep-fried.
21. A foam made of beaten egg whites and sugar.
22. Small, flat cookies usually eaten alone and rarely used as a component in other desserts.

B. Short Answer

1. a. chiffon   b. cooked juice   c. cream

2. a. cream   b. chiffon   b. cooked juice   d. cheesecake
3. a. baked fruit   b. custard
4. a. lattice coverings
   b. pie top crusts
   c. prebaked shells later to be filled with cooked fillings
5. It is a rich, non-flaky, and sturdier dough than flaky or mealy dough due to the addition of egg yolks and the blending of the fat.
6. When the crust has a potential of becoming soggy, as in the making of custard and cooked fruit pies.
7. One can have better control because you can feel the fat being incorporated and therefore prevent overmixing.
8. It is cooked before baking.
9. The ratio of sugar to egg whites.
10. a. vol au vents   c. feuilletées
    b. Napoleons   d. bouchées

C. Multiple Choice

1. d   4. c
2. b   5. d
3. b

D. True or False

1. True (p. 831)
2. False (p. 819) Strawberries, pineapples, and blueberries would be more appropriate.
3. True (p. 817)
4. True (p. 821)
5. False (p. 816) A typical ratio for crumb crusts consists of one part melted butter to two parts sugar to four parts crumbs.
6. True (p. 816)
7. False (p. 810) Pâte sucrée should be used specifically over flaky and mealy doughs because it is less flaky and due to the addition of the egg yolks is still tender, but is stronger to withstand the removal of the tart pan during service.
8. True (p. 881)

CHAPTER 30

A. Terminology

1. Royal icing
2. Butter cakes
3. Buttercream
4. Stencil
5. Icing
6. Chiffon cakes
7. Spongecakes
8. Glucose

9. A cooked mixture of water and sugar which is applied warm to the cake.
10. A blend of melted chocolate and cream with is used as a frosting.
11. A creaming method cake that is made up of a pound of each ingredient: flour, butter, eggs, and sugar.
12. A creaming method cake that requires emulsified shortenings and liquids that are added in two stages.
13. Applying decoration to the sides of the cake.
14. A whipped egg cake made by whipping whole eggs and sugar, adding the dry ingredients, and folding in melted butter or oil.
15. A fat-free whipped egg cake, which uses a large amount of egg whites for leavening.

B. Basic Cake Mixes Revised

Reference: Pages 860–867

C. Matching

1. f
2. a
3. e
4. c
5. d
6. g

D. Cake Mixing Categories

1. b
2. b
3. a
4. b
5. a
6. a
7. a
8. b
9. a
10. a

E. Frostings Revised

Reference: Pages 872–880

F. Fill in the Blank

1. decreased
   underwhipped
   increased
   25 degrees
2. a. high fat
   creamed fat
   b. egg foam
   whipped eggs
3. 325°F
   375°F
4. decorators icing

5. flour
   shortening
   oil

G. True or False

1. False (p. 871) All cakes should be left away from drafts which may cause them to collapse. Cakes should not be refrigerated as rapid cooling will cause cracking.
2. True (p. 887)
3. True (p. 870)
4. True (p. 871)
5. False (p. 865)
6. True (p. 868)
7. False (p. 868) The results from package mixes are consistent and acceptable to most customers.
8. False (p. 861) High-ratio cakes require emulsified shortenings to absorb the large amounts of sugar and liquid in the formula.

CHAPTER 31

A. Terminology

1. Sundae
2. Temper
3. Sorbet
4. Steep
5. Baked Alaska
6. Sabayon
7. Overrun
8. Soufflé
9. Bombe
10. Crème Chantilly
11. Ice cream served with a fruit topping
12. An egg custard made with egg yolks, sugar, and milk and thickened with starch.
13. An ice cream that has little incorporated air.
14. A sauce made from a mixture of egg yolks, sugar, and milk or half and half, cooked over low heat, which may be served either hot or cold.
15. Ice cream served in a long slender glass with alternate layers of topping or sauce.
16. A mousse is softer than a Bavarian or chiffon, is generally too soft to mold and can be served alone or used as a filling in cakes.
17. A frozen mousselike dessert, usually chocolate.
18. A round mold lined with spongecake or ladyfingers, filled with a Bavarian cream, and chilled.
19. A three-layered loaf or cake of ice cream, each layer a different flavor.
20. A Bavarian cream is prepared by first thickening custard sauce with gelatin and then folding in whipped cream.

21. A chiffon is most often used as a pie filling and is similar to a Bavarian except that whipped egg whites (instead of whipped cream) are folded into the thickened base of custard or a fruit mixture thickened with cornstarch.

B. Short Answer

1. Reference: Page 902
2. Reference: Page 903
3. Reference: Page 915
4. Reference: Page 919

C. Fill in the Blank

1. zabaglione
2. mousseline
   Italian merangue
3. Bavarians
   chiffons
   mousses
   crèmes Chantilly
4. a. egg whites will whip to a better volume
   b. the two mixtures are more easily incorporated

D. True or False

1. False (p. 903)
2. True (p. 908) A frozen soufflé is a creamy custard mixture thickened with gelatin, lightened with whipped egg whites or whipped cream, and placed in a soufflé dish wrapped with a tall paper collar.
3. False (p. 916) A sherbet contains milk and/or egg yolks for creaminess.
4. True (p. 917)
5. True (p. 917)
6. True (p. 906)

CHAPTER 32

A. Terminology

1. Shirred eggs
2. Granola
3. Quiche
4. French toast
5. Omelets
6. Thin, delicate, unleavened pancakes cooked in a small, very hot sauté pan.
7. An open-faced omelet of Spanish-Italian origin, which is cooked in a small pan and may be finished in the oven or under a salamander.
8. A leavened batter that is cooked on a waffle iron and forms square, griddle-like, crisp shapes.

9. This egg dish is a variation of sunny-side-up eggs. The eggs are cooked in a pan over low heat with butter spooned over them as they cook.
10. A leavened batter cooked on a very hot griddle with very little fat, usually served with flavored butter, fruit compote, or syrup.

B. Short Answer

1. Reference: Page 938–945
2. Reference: Page 939
3. A cheese blintz is a crepe that is cooked on only one side and is filled with cheese, browned in butter, and served with sour cream, fruit compote, or preserves.
4. Reference: Page 941

C. True or False

1. False (p. 936) Breakfast should provide at least one-fourth of the calories or nutrients consumed during the day.
2. True (p. 943)
3. True (p. 943)
4. True (p. 943)
5. True (p. 945)
6. False (p. 645) Canadian bacon is very lean and requires very little cooking.
7. True (p. 948)
8. False (p. 941) Fillings for omelettes should be cooked before being added to the omelet, otherwise the egg will be cooked while the filling is still raw.

CHAPTER 33

A. Terminology

1. Osetra
2. Sushi
3. Beluga
4. Chafing dish
5. Sevruga
6. Sashimi
7. Brochettes
8. Crudités
9. Canapés
10. The eggs of chum and silver salmon, a very popular garnish, these are large with a good flavor and a natural orange color
11. The French term which translates to "outside work."
12. A readily available caviar that is reasonably priced, this caviar is dyed black, red, or gold.
13. This caviar is made by allowing the moisture to drain from osetra and sevruga; it has a jamlike consistency.
14. A tiny boat-shaped shell made from savory dough such as pâte or brisée.

15. A caviar from sturgeon found in the waters of the Northwest and the Tennessee River, which is relatively low in price.
16. Bacon wrapped around chicken livers, olives, pickled watermelon rind, water chestnuts, pineapple, or scallops.
17. The small and very crisp eggs of whitefish native to the northern Great Lakes.

B. Multiple Choice

1. d
2. b
3. c
4. b

C. Fill in The Blanks

1. a thin slice of bread cut into an interesting shape and toasted
   vegetables
2. flavored butter
   cream cheese
   salads
   egg
   chicken
3. Malasol
   little salt
4. two weeks
   taste
5. mayonnaise
   sour cream
   cream cheese
   milk
   buttermilk
   cream or sour cream
6. béchamel
   cream sauce
   cheese sauce
   bagna cauda
7. soak them in water
8. an Asian noodle dough used to make egg rolls
   pork, chicken, shellfish, and vegetables

D. Short Answer

1. Reference: Page 962
2. Reference: Page 964
3. Reference: Page 967
4. Reference: Page 975

E. True or False

1. False (p. 962 & p. 975) Appetizers are usually the first course before the evening meal.

2. True (p. 965)
3. True (p. 965)
4. False (p. 965) Caviar reacts with metal, producing off flavors.
5. False (p. 967) Fish used for sushi should preferably be no more than one day old.
6. False (p. 970) Barquettes should be filled at the last minute, otherwise they become soggy.

CHAPTER 34

A. Terminology

1. Professional cooking
2. Cookery
3. Ethnic cuisine
4. The ingredients, seasonings, cooking procedures and styles, and eating habits attributed to a particular group of people.
5. A set of recipes based upon local ingredients, traditions, and practices, which often blend together to create a national cuisine.
6. The characteristic cuisine of a nation.

B. Short Answer

1. Reference: Page 998–1002
   Northern China: Dry climate—rice cannot grow, therefore wheat and millet, eaten as noodles, dumplings, and pancakes, are popular.
   Eastern China: The fertile year-round growing season provides more vegetables for the regions' chefs than anywhere else in China.
   Southern China: Canton is a fertile region which produces exotic seafood and a wide variety of fruits and vegetables. The region emphasizes freshness and therefore stir-frying is the predominant cooking method.
2. Reference: Page 1002
   a. Eastern China has adopted slow cooking from European culture.
   b. Eastern China has also adopted some dairy products, which are rarely used elsewhere in China.
   c. The Chinese have adopted the appetizer from the Americans and the Europeans.
3. Reference: Page 1004
   a. Japan is made up of islands, therefore there is access to the sea.
   b. Buddhist teachings promote the consumption of vegetables and seafood.
4. Reference: Pages 1014 & 1016
   a. Traditionally Mexican cuisine relied upon steaming and slow cooking; however, since the conquest of Mexico by the Spanish, sautéing and pan-frying have become commonplace.
   b. Mexican sauce making is very different from the European methods.

C. Matching

1. d   4. f
2. a   5. c
3. b   6. g

D. Multiple Choice

1. a
2. d
3. c
4. d
5. c

E. Fill in the Blank

1. nouvelle cuisine
2. red cooking
3. rice, dals, and bread
   dals
4. pork
   beef
   meat, poultry, shellfish, or dairy products
5. wheat
6. chiles
7. masala
8. Tandoori chicken
   clay
   dry

F. True or False

1. True (p. 998)
2. True (p. 998 & 1002)
3. True (p. 1007)
4. False (p. 1005) Curry powder is a commercial masala that is never used in true Indian cooking.
5. True (p. 1010)
6. False (p. 1015) The ancient cooking method of steaming meats is still used in modern Mexico.

CHAPTER 35

A. Terminology

1. The process of delivering the selected foods to diners in the proper fashion.
2. A food product that adds an attractive visual aspect to a plate presentation but also provides complementing flavor to the main item on the plate.
3. Presentation
4. Composition

B. Fill in the Blank

1. Hippen masse
2. Texture, shape, color

3. Cutting, molding
4. Size
5. Focal point
6. a. Flavor   d. Color
   b. Moisture   e. Texture
   c. Flow
7. Cold
8. a. Height
   b. Texture
9. a. To show the chef's attention to detail
   b. To provide visual appeal
   c. To ensure even cooking of the product

C. True or False

1. True (p. 1024)
2. False (p. 1027) The food should always be the focal point of any plate.
3. True (p. 1027)
4. False (p. 1028) Dusting of a plate should be done before the food is plated.
5. False (p. 1032) A squeeze bottle would be a good choice of equipment for preparing sauce drawings.
6. False (p. 1031) An equally important concept is that the sauces need to be thick enough to hold a pattern and all sauces used in the drawing need to be the same viscosity.